THE
WHICH?
GUIDE TO BUYING
COLLECTABLES

THE
WHICH?
GUIDE TO BUYING
COLLECTABLES

DUNCAN CHILCOTT

Which?
BOOKS
Published by Consumers' Association and Hodder & Stoughton

CONTENTS

The Which? Guide to Buying Collectables was commissioned by The Association for Consumer Research and published by Consumers' Association, 2 Marylebone Road, London NW1 4DX and Hodder & Stoughton, 47 Bedford Square, London WC1B 3DP

Copyright © 1991 Consumers' Association Limited
First edition October 1991

British Library Cataloguing in Publication Data
Chilcott, Duncan
The Which? guide to buying collectables.
1. Antiques. Great Britain
I. Title II. Consumers' Association
745.1

ISBN 0 340 55005 8

Conceived and produced by Michael Stephenson Publishing.

Index by Jill Ford.

Typeset by Holywell Graphics, London.

Printed and bound in Hong Kong by Oceanic Graphic Printing Inc.

Cover illustrations: clockwise from top left: A collection of ceramic busts of politicians, 19th and 20th centuries, *£50-300 each.* A Copeland 'subscriber's copy' loving cup commemorating the Transvaal war of 1899-1900, *£1,050.* A collection of toys, including a German bisque-headed doll, *c.* 1900, *£400.* A chromed car mascot, *c.* 1930, *£80.* Pre-World War II cigarette cards, *£15 each set.* Lead toy soldiers ('Roman Triumph') by C.B.G. Mignot, 1890, *£80 the set.* A Steiff dark-gold plush teddy bear, *c.* 1910, *£700.* *Illustrations page 3, from left to right:* A magazine advertising insert, *c.* 1900. *£12-20.* A late 19th-century stoneware whisky jug with stopper, transfer advertisement under the glaze, 9in (23cm) high. *£100-200.* 1920s kitchen scales advertising the 'Household Encyclopedia'. *£20-30.*

INTRODUCTION

The term 'collectables' takes in under its umbrella such bygones as pipes, cigarette cards, kitchen implements, tools, toys and pens. Whereas an antique may not earn its title until it is 100 years old, quite modern objects can legitimately be called collectables. Although most collectable items cannot honestly be regarded as fine art, they capture our imagination with the beauty of their craftsmanship and they transport us back to a world which seems more innocent and less complicated than our own. In addition, they evoke both the people who made them and those who used them. This is not to say that all collectables are cheap or in some way merely marginal as works of art. The quality (and price tag!) of a fine nineteenth-century guitar, or a Lalique car mascot, or a Jacobite drinking glass, put them in the upper echelon of craftsmanship and collecting. And although the middle ground predominates in this guide, the reader will also find a rare set of eighteenth-century drawing instruments at £18,000, as well as a button for £1.

This book will introduce to the reader a considered assortment of some already established collecting themes, together with a sample of more recent trends. For example, suits of armour, cavalry swords and groups of medals have been in demand for many years by collectors of militaria, while jukeboxes, bakelite radios and twentieth-century furniture are still in their infancy in the collecting world.

At the same time there has been no attempt to cover the complete spectrum of collecting. To represent every possible collectable theme in this style and format would require thousands of photographs and many volumes. One day someone may compile the definitive work on collectables, starting with 'Abacus-iana' (early mathematical calculators of Ancient Greece), and finishing with 'Zythum-alia' (Egyptian beer memorabilia of the first century BC)!

Within these parameters the book considers as many angles to a particular theme as possible. The automobilia section, for instance, includes car badges and mascots; less obvious, but equally important, are the diversionary examples of motoring jewellery and Sir Clive Sinclair's C5. The jewellery brooch in the form of a vintage motorcar reminds us that early motoring was a pastime enjoyed only by the wealthy. The C5, on the other hand, was an attempt to produce a budget-priced electric vehicle for the mass market; although an heroic failure, it undoubtedly represents a future piece of collectable automobilia. At the time of writing, the average price is around £200, a great deal less than most automobilia.

As a national pastime, collecting took off in the last quarter of the nineteenth century. The Victorians collected just about anything and everything from anywhere. Theirs was an age of discovery and learning, and their confident inquisitiveness, combined with wealth generated by the Industrial Revolution, enabled many adventurers to travel around the world, particularly the British Empire, exploring, discovering and collecting as they went. Antiquities from North Africa and Europe, Renaissance paintings and sculpture, tribal art and other treasures from across the seas began to be accumulated along with stuffed exotic birds and animals, birds' eggs, butterflies and a wide range of flora.

The style of collecting 100 years later is very different. The last quarter of the twentieth century has witnessed a rather nostalgic movement. Quality and style are back in demand, resulting in the legitimisation of Victoriana, together with a renewed interest in antique accessories such as fountain pens, wristwatches and jewellery.

So, where can you go to start collecting? There is actually nothing very scientific about collecting antiques and bygones. Most collectors stumble across their chosen subjects by chance. Some simply continue collections that they have acquired or inherited. Others gradually build up collections of objects and memorabilia associated with a theme or themes that are of interest to them.

Let us suppose you want to start collecting postcards, for example. As postcard-collecting in Britain is second in popularity only to stamp-collecting it is very well organised. Periodicals such as *Postcard Monthly* contain informative articles and collecting tips about postcards, both old and new. A number of useful annual postcard price-guides present the main collecting themes and include essential advice on condition and rarity. A good selection of reference books, usually of a more specialist nature, cover individual themes in detail.

Auctions

Some people, especially beginners, entering an auction room for the first time, are nervous of procedures, conditions and what surcharges may be levied. As these vary from auction house to auction house, go to the information desk and ask for the conditions of sale.

Selling at auction

The hammer price (i.e. the price realised) is not what the seller receives. The auctioneer's commission (about 10 per cent is normal) and VAT (estimated on the auctioneer's commission, not the hammer price) will be deducted. A specialist at an auction house may suggest that you allow your piece to be illustrated in a forthcoming catalogue. Although this may cost you several pounds (it varies, obviously, according to whether the photograph is to be in colour or black-and-white), it will almost invariably result in a higher sale price, which will more than compensate you for the cost. The auction house may also levy a charge for insurance (on average, one per cent of the realised price).

Buying at auction

When bidding on a lot, make your first bid very obvious by putting your hand in the air. Once you have attracted the auctioneer's attention in this way, you can continue to bid by nodding your head or waving the catalogue. The idea that you can have a lot knocked down to you because of an inadvertent blink or gesture is a myth. If you want to bid on a lot but cannot attend the auction, most auctioneers are happy to accept a 'commission bid' from you. This empowers the auctioneer to make your bid for you. It is easy to get carried away by the excitement of an auction, so set financial limits on the lots in which you are interested. Buyers, too, will be charged a commission (again, usually about 10 per cent of the hammer price). And VAT will apply to that commission.

Whatever you intend to collect, whether postcards, perfume bottles or penny-farthings, you should read up on the subject first. It benefits the collector to understand something of the subject to begin with, and it may help to avoid mistakes. For example, if you collected Stevengraph pictures and were offered a woven silk commemorative portrait of Queen Elizabeth II and Prince Philip, dated 1953, before parting with any money it would help you to know that:

• Stevengraph silk pictures were not produced after World War II

• a few woven silk pictures were produced after 1945 by other manufacturers, but were never very popular

• a 1953 Coronation commemorative silk picture is probably quite rare, regardless of who produced it.

As well as reading up about your interest, you could join a local collecting club. Most major towns and cities have such clubs. Here collectors meet regularly in a friendly atmosphere, and often invite guest speakers to talk on a variety of subjects. Fellow collectors are often mines of information and are usually very happy to help novices.

Once you have researched your particular subject, now is the time to take a cautious foray into the marketplace. In most cases you will be spoilt for choice: many auction houses, dealers and specialist fairs cater to the requirements of the collector. Each provides a range of services and facilities.

The fine art auction houses, particularly those based in London, have made great efforts in recent years to present sales of collectables in such a way as to make them equally accessible to private collectors and dealers. In addition to auctions of the standard collectable items – for example toys and dolls, cameras and photographs, fountain pens and writing equipment, sporting memorabilia, postcards and cigarette cards, textiles and samplers, entertainment memorabilia and militaria – many of the fine art departments prepare 'theme'- auctions, including marine art and ship models, perfume bottles, Lalique glass, Staffordshire pottery and pot-lids, commemorative china and collectable books.

It is advisable to contact each auction house and enquire about the nature of its collectors' auctions. Subscribing to the auction sale catalogues will guarantee that you receive all details of forthcoming sales. The typical cost for this service (including the cost of the catalogue) is around £20 per year. Develop a relationship with the staff of the auction houses. Again, you will discover that they are either collectors or enthusiasts themselves, and are willing to offer professional advice.

Dealers also offer an invaluable service, and a friendly dealer is the collector's greatest ally. Let your local dealers know of your collecting passions, and inform them of any specific requirements. A dealer will look after a good customer, making concessions in price to a regular buyer whose business he or she values.

As the interest in collectables grows, so the number of antiques fairs increases. Weekend antique and craft fairs, car-boot sales, and even jumble sales, make splendid hunting grounds. Perseverance and dedication are the keys to successful collecting, and many collectors admit that they experience as much enjoyment from 'the chase' as they do from possessing the treasured piece.

Once you have started collecting, what should you look for? This book does not presume to tell you what to collect but does put forward some ideas. However, whatever you do choose, the advice is the same. The condition of antiques and collectable items is very important. The better the condition, the more valuable is the item. Always try to obtain the best example possible, and never allow yourself to be attracted by quantity in favour of quality. One perfect example is far more satisfactory than a ragbag of chipped, restored or broken pieces. In any case, good pieces are likely to appreciate in value more quickly than damaged examples, so are much easier to sell if you ever want to do so.

A necessary ancillary to a collection is its records. It is both interesting and important to keep adequate records of the purchase of various items — the price paid, information about collections of which they may previously have been part, and so on. It is also a good idea to include information on similar examples that are subsequently sold by other collectors, and on items featured in various publications. Such information adds a further dimension to your enjoyment, and may add to the value of your collection.

A photographic record to complement the written record has a great deal to commend it. In this way, the collector does much valuable work for posterity, while at the same time making the replacement of broken or stolen pieces through insurance much easier.

Insuring a collection of antiques or collectables against loss is obviously a good idea. However, insurance companies vary in their attitudes to insuring works of art.

Prices

The prices given in this guide are, wherever possible, based on an actual price realised at auction within the year preceding publication. In some cases, however, a price-band has been used where a piece does not have an auction sale price. It is very important to realise that all prices relating to collectables and antiques are somewhat fluid and are influenced by several factors. The auction price is at least a known benchmark, but it is not necessarily the price you will find at a dealer's or in a private sale. The dealer (who also buys at auction, among other places) has to build in a margin to cover overheads (the rental of premises, advertising, running costs and so on) as well as a profit margin. On the other hand you may find similar articles to those in this book at a cheaper price because you are buying from a private individual who has no such overheads. Changing fashions and tastes also influence price, so the would-be collector should check specialist publications and visit auctions and dealers regularly to get a feeling for price levels. As most dealers will tell you, it is the ignorant and fearful or the cockily half-knowledgeable customers who are the most difficult.

Some refuse to insure valuable pottery and porcelain against damage unless it is kept locked away, while others may insist that collectors of silver and jewellery fit special locks or burglar alarms. It is best to seek advice of insurers who have some experience in this field.

While considerations of such as records and insurance are important, do not forget that, above all, collecting is meant to be fun. It will lead you to meet many interesting and occasionally delightfully eccentric people. In the quest for an elusive example, you will have to visit unusual places, often off the beaten track. And in addition to all this there will be the collection itself to enjoy.

Duncan Chilcott

ADVERTISING BYGONES

The use of trade signs to advertise skills and products goes back to Roman times. Since then tradespeople have used permanent and ephemeral advertisements of many kinds. The Victorians were the first to spend vast sums on advertising, using the enamelled sign (permanent) and the poster (ephemeral). Pears was one of the first companies in the field; it consistently updated its adverts, and these now present the collector with a specialist subject in itself.

Victorian advertisements were loosely inserted in magazines, and were later printed in the newspapers themselves. Jugs, figures and ashtrays with slogans were used extensively in pubs by distilleries and brewers, and together with 'gifts' bearing the advertiser's name and slogan offer a wide range for the collector, from book-matches to whist-scorers.

Most collectors specialise in such a diverse field, concentrating on, say, posters of a given period or subject, or advertising ceramics from Wedgwood, Doulton or Minton. For example, a Carltonware ceramic Guinness toucan of the 1930s can fetch £100 at auction.

A Waterman Pen Co. advertising postcard depicting the famous cricketer Jack Hobbs. £5.

A 1930s printed-tin shop-counter advertising calendar made by The Metal Box Co. for 'Radio Times'. 9¼ x 14⅓in (23.75 x 36.25cm). £40-60.

PUB ADVERTISING:
Above, clockwise from far left:
Beefeater Extra Dry Gin,
15in (37cm) high. *£100.*

Courvoisier Brandy
'Napoleon', 13in (32.5cm)
high. *£120.*

Drambuie 'Bonnie Prince
Charlie', 16in (40cm) high.
£80.

Double Diamond
polychrome Beswick figure,
8¼in (21cm) high. *£100.*

Martell Brandy stylised
Carltonware figure, 8½in
(21.25cm) high. *£120.*

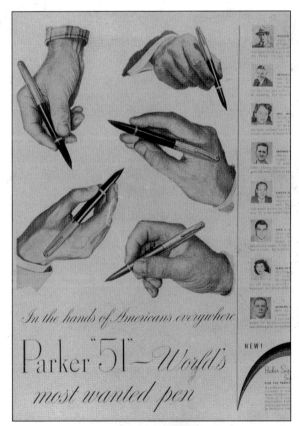

Left: 1947 'Time' magazine
advertisement for Parker
pens. *£15.*

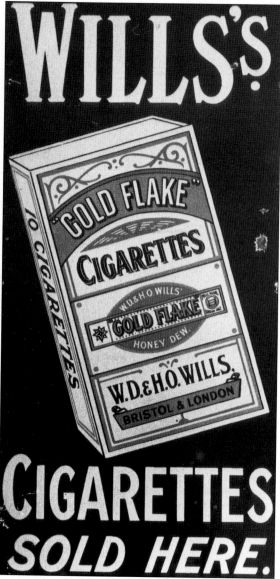

Above: Enamelled-metal sign, 'Wills's Cigarettes', *c.* 1930, in six colours, 26½ x 18in (66 x 45cm). *£75-100.*

Above, right: Enamelled-metal sign, 'The Rajah Cigar' *c.* 1905, in blue, white, red and brown, 18½ x 10in (46 x 25cm). *£250-350.*

Right: Bar water-jug, 'Younger for You', Doulton, black-and-white transfer decoration. *£50.*

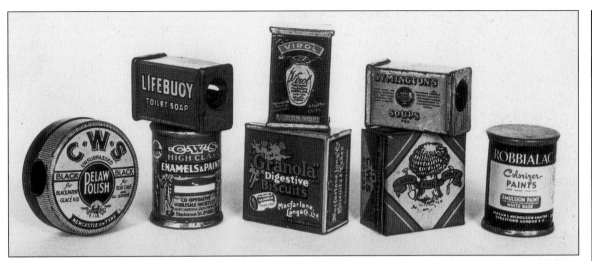

Above: Miniature tins and pencil sharpeners advertising various products, 1920-30s, 1in (2.5cm) longest dimension. *£15-30 each.*

Above: Points-scorer for whist, cream-coloured celluloid with multicoloured printing and advertiser's trademark 'Molassine', *c.* 1930. *£25.*

Left: Bar water-jug for 'McNish' whisky, with multicoloured tartan pattern, *c.* 1920. *£40.*

Below: Loose magazine insert, 'Pears' Shaving Soap', black and two-coloured print, 19th century. *£12.*

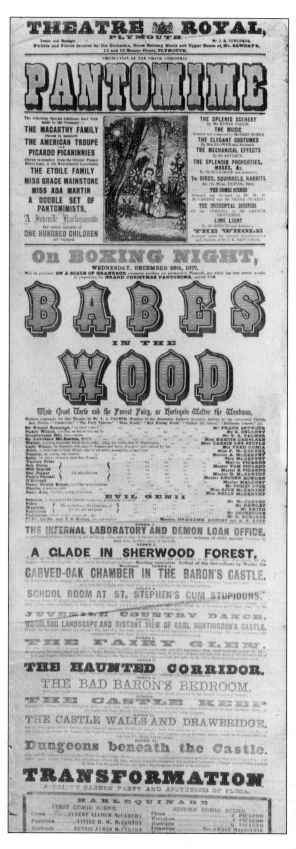

Right: Theatre poster, 'Babes in the Wood', Theatre Royal, Plymouth, with pictorial insert, 1877. *£75.*

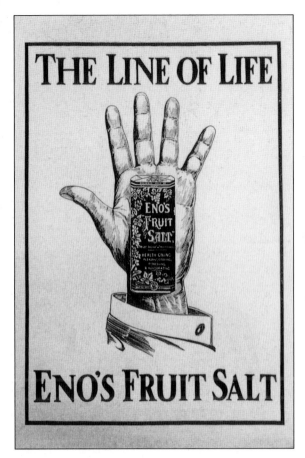

Left: Loose magazine insert, 'Eno's Fruit Salt', black print, 19th century. £10.

Above: Pot-lid for cold cream, with name and address of local retailer, 19th century. £65.

Below: A 19th-century local business card, engraved and typeset in black. £15.

Above: Bottle label, 'A.1. Ginger Ale', multicoloured printing, c. 1860. £1-2.

Pottery change tray, 'Mason's Ironstone', advertising manufacturer's own ware, *c.* 1930. *£12.*

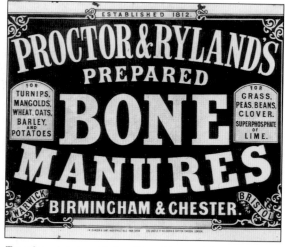

Transfer-printed metal sign, 'Bone Manures', for agricultural suppliers, blue on cream, *c.* 1920, 14 x 18in (35 x 45cm). *£45.*

A late Victorian Fry's Chocolate stained-glass advertising panel, 44in (112cm) high. *£950.*

'Parfums Fontanis', a rare gilt-copper advertising plaque, *c.* 1920, 3¾ x 4⅜in (9.4 x 12cm), in fitted case. *£1,900.*

Opposite: A multicoloured painted-plaster figure of an ice-cream girl, with retailer's name on base, *c.* 1930, approx. 20in (50cm) high. *£200-300.*

ANTIQUITIES

Covering the art and artefacts of the ancient world, antiquities, generally speaking, have to be at least 1,000 years old. Most span the period from about 7,000 BC to AD 500, but some from as late as the early medieval period can also qualify. Most of the objects available for sale come from the ancient civilisations of Europe (mainly Greece and Rome), Egypt and the Near East (Mesopotamia and Persia, for example).

In Britain, the fashion for collecting antiquities started in the 18th century when well-bred young men were customarily sent on the Grand Tour of Italy. No such tour would have been thought complete without an impressive haul of ancient artefacts and sculpture. Today, even the least aristocratic of us may indulge, and often for far less money than one would perhaps at first have thought. For example, a Roman bronze strigil (an implement used to remove oil after a bath) can be bought for around £300. Roman glass vessels of various shapes, sizes and functions might cost as little as £90 (on the other hand, they can cost thousands!), and pottery from a variety of civilisations can be acquired from about £150.

The range of artefacts on the market is enormous: ancient Persian weaponry, Roman lamps, Egyptian tools, or wearable Roman gold earrings can be had for £200. The most expensive areas tend to be ancient Egyptian and Minoan pieces because they are not only the most popular but also the rarest. The craftsmanship that went into these ancient artefacts is usually of superb quality and very often the techniques used are extremely sophisticated. In addition, the thrill of being able to hold something that links us to the very dawn of civilisation is an exciting experience.

Above: A bronze Amlash shaft-hole axe-adze, *c.* 1,200 BC, 6¾in (17cm), with special display mount. *£150.*

Above: An Attic red-figure trefoil lipped olpe, with profile ladies' heads facing each other across a stylised palmette, 4th century BC, 6¼in (10cm). *£500.*

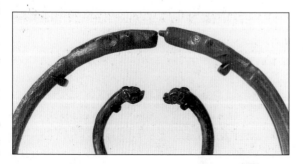

Left, top: An Iranian bronze torque, the ribbed hoop terminating in dogs' heads with inlaid silver eyes, 1st millennium BC, 5¼in (13.3cm) diam. *£160.*

Left, bottom: A Luristan silver bracelet, with terminals of lions' heads, Western Iran, 8th-7th century BC, 2⅛in (5.4cm) diam., mounted on a stand. *£150.*

Above: A multi-coloured fragment of Coptic textile, its central panel with fruit-laden tree, with outer stylised wave pattern, 7 x 6½in (17.75 x 16cm). *£95.*

Above: An Egyptian half-collar, of glazed composition beads, with a row of gilded drops, *c.* 300 BC, 3in (8cm) depth. *£80.*

Above: A section of Roman coloured mosaic, Eastern Empire, 3rd-4th century AD, 81¼ x 16½in (206 x 42cm). *£300.*

Left: A green glazed composition Ushabti figure, with tripartite wig, pick and hoe in hands and basket over left shoulder hanging from a cord, a single line of hieroglyphs in the front panel, plain dorsal pillar, Late Period, 30th Dynasty, 380-43 BC, 6¼in (16cm) high. *£400.*

Above: A marble memorial tablet with the inscription, 'Set up by Tiberius Claudius Januarius [in memory] of Platia Fortunata, his admirable wife', probably from Rome, end of 1st century AD, 7 x 9in (17.8 x 22.8cm). *£500.*

ART DECO FIGURINES

Until quite recently the prices paid today for bronze-and-ivory figures would have been unthinkable. In fact Art Deco figurines were generally regarded as, at worst, examples of poor taste, and at best kitsch.

Chryselephine sculpture, i.e. the combination of ivory with other materials such as wood, marble and bronze, was made popular by Belgian artists in the 1890s and came to be treated as expensive art. It was not until the first decade of the 20th century that such sculpture became more widely available. As a result of mass-production techniques the cast-bronze figures with hand-carved heads, bodies

and limbs became widely popular and fashionable, and by the 1930s the figures had developed into a pure Deco style. The outbreak of World War II signalled the end of the popularity of bronze-and-ivory figures, and interest lay dormant for the following three decades, only to be rekindled recently.

Demetre Chiparus and Ferdinand Preiss are regarded by dealers and collectors alike as masters of bronze-and-ivory figures. Chiparus's major preoccupation seems to have been with Egyptian themes, characterised by sleek and chic figures. Preiss figures possess an incredible realism, sometimes enhanced by skin tints.

Far left and right: A pair of Art Deco bronze figures, each modelled as a rearing horse, one ridden by a stylised female figure, the other by a male, 14½in (37cm) high, not signed. £800.

Top left: 'Moth Girl', a bronze-and-ivory figure cast and carved from a model by Ferdinand Preiss, the girl wearing a tight-fitting suit and a hat with antennae, 16¼in (41.5cm) high, marked 'F. Preiss'. £2,500.

Bottom centre: 'Pursuits of Youth', a pair of cold-painted bronze-and-ivory bookends, cast and carved from a model by Ferdinand Preiss, 6¾in (17cm) high, engraved 'F. Preiss'. £1,500.

Top right: A bronze figure, the design attributed to Cl. J. R. Colinet, 15½in (39.5cm) high. £800.

Below: 'Javelin Thrower', a cold-painted bronze-and-ivory figure, cast and carved from a model by Ferdinand Preiss, 12⅛in (31cm) high. *£4,000-6,000.*

Above: 'The Respectful Splits', a cold-painted bronze-and-ivory figure, cast from a model by Paul Philippe on a green onyx rectangular base, 7in (18cm) high, signed 'P. Philippe'. *£2,000.*

Right, from left to right: A bronze figural lamp, cast from a model by G. Flamand, 8¼in (21cm) high, inscribed 'G. Flamand', stamped 'A. Bastet Lyon'. *£900.*

A gilt-bronze figure, cast from a model by Schmidt-Hofer, standing on a square veined-marble base, 9in (23cm) high, inscribed 'Schmidt-Hofer'. *£250.*

A gilt-bronze figure, cast from a model by Joe Descomps, 17¾in (45cm) high, base signed 'Joe Descomps'. *£1,110.*

Above, from left to right:
A silvered-bronze figure, cast from a model by Lorenzl, 22⅜in (58cm) high, marked 'Lorenzl'. £2,400.

A green-patinated bronze figure of a semi-nude young woman cast from a model by Lorenzl, 11½in (29cm) high, diam. of dish 10½in (27cm), figure signed 'Lorenzl'. £920.

A cold-painted bronze group, cast from a model by Lorenzl, as two figures from the Ballets Russes, the young man kneeling to support his female partner, on stepped rectangular bronze and green onyx base, 11½in (29.2cm) high, signed 'Lorenzl'. £1,000.

'Bubble Dancer', a bronze-and-ivory figure, cast and carved from a model by Ferdinand Preiss, the young girl wearing a short tunic, standing on tiptoes, her arms outstretched, holding a glass bubble on an octagonal stepped veined black-marble base, with four cream-marble segments, 20½in (52cm), base inscribed 'Godard'. £6,000.

A bronze-and-ivory figure cast and carved from a model by Ferdinand Preiss, on marble socle, 7in (17.5cm), engraved 'F. Preiss' and founder's mark. £480.

A green-patinated bronze figure, cast from a model by Henri Fugère, 19in (48cm), base signed 'H. Fugère'. £900.

A gilt-bronze figure, cast from a model by Lorenzl, the dancing nude female figure balancing on her right foot, on black marble column, 24¼in (61.5cm) high, marked 'Lorenzl'. £2,400.

Right: A cold-painted bronze-and-ivory figure by Lorenzl, the young woman wearing a close-fitting long dress with split skirt and elaborate collar and cuffs, stepping out on a green onyx and black marble stepped oval base, 11in (28cm) high, inscribed 'Lorenzl'. £600.

Above: A Limousin bronzed-metal figure, the nude young woman poised on her right foot, left knee raised, a drape held over her outstretched arms, on pierced pyramidal base, 15½in (39.5cm) high, inscribed 'par Limousin'. £200.

Above: A pair of gilt-bronze and-ivory figures by G. Omer, each standing on chamfered square marble bases, 8¾in (22.5cm) and 9½in (24cm) high, both signed 'G. Omer'. £800-1,200.

Right: 'Innocence', a cold-painted bronze-and-ivory figure cast and carved from a model by Demetre Chiparus, 14½in (37cm) high, base engraved 'D. Chiparus'. £2,900.

AUTOMOBILIA

The history of automobilia extends back as far as the horseless carriage, with companies such as Alfred Dunhill, Hermès and Louis Vuitton providing blankets, coats, goggles and, most importantly, picnic trunks and tonneaux for the discerning motorist. Today, an early Dunhill or Finnigans motoring trunk can be found for as little as £50, while a high-quality Vickers trunk with china and silver fittings will cost the collector around £1,000.

Motorcar accessories were equally important to early motorists, and are keenly sought-after by collectors today. Marchal road lamps are currently realising £1,000 for a pair, while Edwardian 'boa constrictor' horns at about £100 are considered the finishing touch to a classic vehicle.

For the armchair collector who does not want an expensive vintage or veteran classic car, there is a wide variety of car mascots and badges, representing the largest collecting area. These are doomed never to return to grace a motorcar, but a collection can be assembled with ease; £50 will buy a simple chromed mascot, or £400 will secure a super sculptural example, but a Le Verrier mascot or a Sykes Rolls Royce Phantom I mascot are commanding prices between £600 to £6,000, as are the glass mascots by Lalique.

A plethora of decorative paintings, prints and photographs of cars of all ages are also on the market. Collectors should expect to pay up to £10,000 for a Gordon Crosby painting, or as little as £20 for an anonymous motoring print.

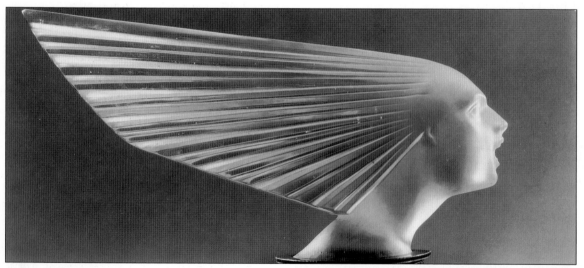

Above: 'Victoire', a satin-glass car mascot, moulded as a female head, mouth open to shout, her streaming hair forming a stiffened wing, on Breves Gallery chromium-plated base, 10in (25.5cm) long, moulded by R. Lalique. *£8,500.*

Right: A vast cigar box, 18 x 12⅔in (46 x 32cm), the hinged cover depicting 'Lautenschlager sur Mercedes, Grand-prix Dieppe de l'A.C.F. 1908' after the tile on the Michelin Building in London, attributed to Ernest Monteaut, bar thumbpiece to hinged cover, on four bun feet, cedar lining to interior. *£720.*

Above, clockwise from far left:
An Austin winged-wheel motorcar mascot, finished in original nickel and stamped 'RD 286069'. *£400.*

An unusual nickel-plated vintage car mascot of a ballroom dancing couple, mounted on period radiator cap, 4in (11cm). *£150.*

An AA Committee Member's motorcar badge with AA flag above chrome-plated badge and yellow back plate, numbered OC59, 6in (16cm). *£150.*

An MG Midget car mascot, with chrome-plated Midget on an octagonal radiator cap (as fitted to pre-war models). *£200.*

A Bentley horizontal winged flying 'B' car mascot with 7in (19cm) wingspan, and stamped 'Joseph Fray B/Ham'. *£200.*

A 'Speed God' car mascot, with the scantily clad figure within a rim of a tyre at speed, signed 'Cottin' and stamped 'R.D. – A.E.L.', 5in (13cm). *£350.*

A Riley Kestrel car mascot, chrome-plated and mounted on a wood base, 5in (13cm). *£120.*

A Rolls Royce 'Spirit of Ecstasy' mascot (for the late 20 HP and early 20/50 series Rolls Royce motorcars) with unusual base and underwing markings, 5in (13cm). *£150.*

A Riley Ski Lady car mascot of plated-bronze finish and stamped 'RD 759377'. *£200.*

Below, left to right:
'Thais', a frosted statuette, the nude female figure with outstretched arms holding pleated drapery behind her, tiptoed on tapering block base, 8⅝in (22cm), engraved 'R. Lalique, France No. 834', *£5,600.*

'Sanglier', a frosted and polished slate-grey car mascot, modelled as a wild boar standing on a circular base, 2⅜in (6.5cm), moulded by R. Lalique, engraved 'France No. 1157'. *£1,000.*

'Coq Houdan', a clear and frosted-glass car mascot, moulded as an upright standing cockerel, on a circular base, 7⅞in (20cm), wheel-cut by R. Lalique, France. *£3,000.*

'Tête de Paon', a frosted and polished-glass car mascot, moulded as a peacock's head, 7in (17.8cm). *£5,000.*

'Sirène', an opalescent car mascot, moulded as a mermaid seated on her coiled tail, her hands arranging her hair, chromium-plated base on rectangular stepped glass base, 4⅛in (10.5cm), moulded by R. Lalique. *£1,600.*

'Faucon', a clear and satin-glass car mascot, the bird perched on a domed base, with metal mount, 6⅛in (16cm), moulded by R. Lalique. *£800.*

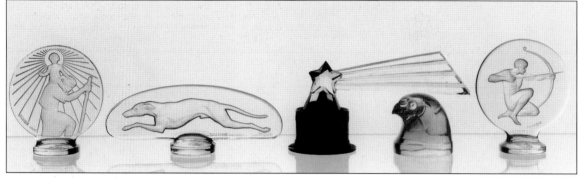

Above, left to right:
'Saint Christophe', a clear and frosted-glass car mascot, the disc intaglio moulded with the saint carrying the young Christ upon his shoulders, amethyst tinted, 4¾in (12cm), moulded by R. Lalique, France. *£900.*

'Lévrier', a clear-glass car mascot, of elliptical panel form, intaglio moulded with a greyhound, 7⅞in (19.7cm) length, moulded by R. Lalique, France. *£2,300.*

'Comet', a clear-glass car mascot, moulded as a shooting star with tapering tail, 7in (18cm) wide, wheel-cut by R. Lalique, France. *£2,000.*

'Têtes d'Eperviers', an opalescent car mascot, moulded as the head of a sparrow-hawk, 2⅝in (6.6cm), moulded by R. Lalique, France. *£2,100.*

'Archer', a clear and frosted car mascot, the disc intaglio moulded with a kneeling male archer, 4⅞in (12.3cm), moulded wheel-cut, R. Lalique, France. *£1,200.*

Below, top row left to right:
A brass 'Telcote Pup' car mascot, *c.* 1930. *£200.*

A large rearing stallion car mascot, on radiator cap and suitable for commercial vehicles. *£120.*

A Speed-Nymph mascot, marked 'REG/ED A.E.L. 656502', on display base, 4in (10cm). *£100.*

A stylised mascot of a leaping female and dog, stamped 'Goddess of Sport', 5in (12.5cm). *£100.*

Below, bottom row left to right:
A Bentley Owners Club badge with red winged Bentley 'B', 4.5in (11cm). *£150.*

A chrome-plated swallow car mascot, with articulated wings, 5in (12.5cm). *£200.*

A nickel-plated brass Vulcan mascot, the figure standing by an anvil, on radiator cap, 4.5in (11cm). *£150.*

An aluminium R.F.C. mascot on stepped base, wingspan 10in (23cm). *£200.*

A Brooklands B.A.R.C. membership badge, enamelled in colours. *£250.*

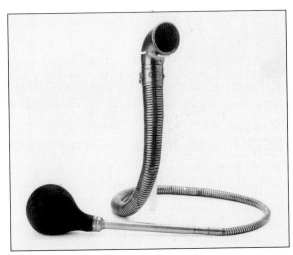

Left: A boa constrictor brass motoring horn, with mesh-covered mouth, articulated tapering body and rubber bulb, 61in (155cm). *£100.*

Below: Jaguar C-Type Le Mans 1953, original black-and-white publicity photograph showing the works C-Type of Jimmy Stewart and P. Whitehead during the early stages of the race, 26 x 19½in (65 x 49cm), framed and glazed. *£150.*

Bottom left: A French Edwardian diamond-set motorcar brooch, the chassis set with diamonds and rose-cut diamonds, in platinum and gold, cabochon ruby light to front, diamond, platinum and gold wheels, possibly by Wilhelm Jung. *£2,200.*

Bottom right: A Sinclair C5 electric-driven trike, *c.* 1984. Though a commercial failure, the C5 was a beautifully engineered and fantastically conceived idea by one of Britain's foremost inventors. *£200.*

BAROMETERS

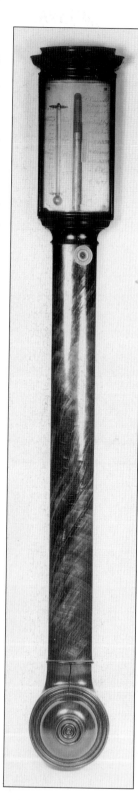

There are four main kinds of barometer: straight or stick, diagonal, wheel and aneroid.

Stick barometers are the earliest type, dating from the 17th century. Early examples mirror the style of contemporary clocks, most having been produced by clock-makers. Later stick barometers developed their own style and reflected the furniture fashions of the day. Prices vary from £700 to £5,000 for a 19th-century specimen, to £25,000 for an early 18th-century example.

Diagonal barometers were developed as a way of making the mercury easier to read. However, due to their ungainly looks they were soon superseded by wheel barometers. Because of their rarity, diagonal barometers realise between £6,000 and £15,000.

The traditional banjo-shaped wheel barometer evolved in the 19th century and is often found with elaborately inlaid mahogany casings and technical advances. A standard Victorian wheel barometer with an 8in dial should cost £700–900, whilst more ornate, larger examples, could cost £7,000.

Aneroid barometers operate without mercury, thus were cheap to produce and could be small. They were made in a variety of shapes, from small 'travelling barometers' to imitation wheel barometers. Prices vary from £1,000 for a rare mid-19th-century aneroid, down to £100 for a turn-of-the-century example.

The functional aspect is important when buying a barometer, and because it would be extremely unusual to find a working one with its original mercury, restoration does not adversely affect the price.

Left: A mahogany bow-fronted stick barometer, signed on the silvered register plates 'L. Casartelli, 136 Duke St., Liverpool', flanked by a thermometer, the flame-figured trunk with turned cistern cover, 37in (94cm). *£1,700.*

Next page, left to right:
A mahogany stick barometer signed on the silvered register plates 'Berrenger, London', glazed door, in a case with architectural pediment and crossbanding to the trunk, 38in (96cm). *£400–500.*

A mahogany stick barometer signed 'Mason, Dublin' on the brass register plate, the glazed door also enclosing a thermometer, in a case with architectural pediment, moulded edges and turned cistern cover, 39in (99cm). *£380–450.*

An inlaid mahogany wheel barometer, the silvered dial signed 'G. Molton, St. Lawrence Step, Norwich', the case with thermometer, architectural pediment, oak leaf and medallion inlays, 39in (99cm). *£250–350.*

An unusual mahogany stick barometer, silvered register plates, flanked by carved beading and scrolls, architectural pediment, fluted trunk, convex fluted cistern cover, 40in (101cm). *£400–500.*

An oak stick barometer, the bone scales signed 'Steward, Strand & Cornhill, London', the arched case with thermometer on the trunk, 39in (99cm). *£350–450.*

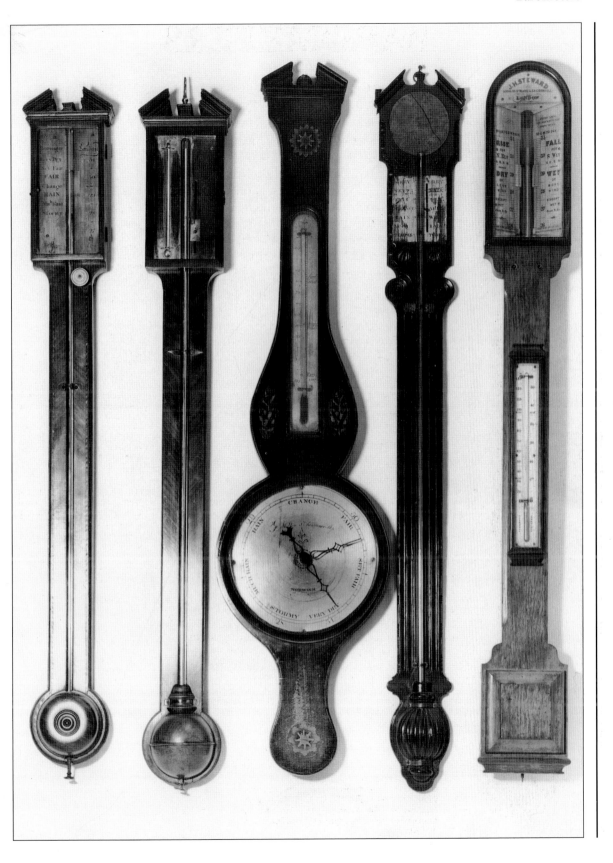

BOTTLES

Although we are used to bottles being made of glass, in the past they were commonly made of stoneware or earthenware. Glass bottles have been produced since antiquity, but the distinctive examples made in England from the 17th to the early 19th centuries represent the mainstream of bottle-collecting today.

Until the mid-17th century, French bottle manufacture was dominant. Afterwards it was the English coal-fired glassmaking techniques that became pre-eminent. These early glass bottles were thick, strong and dark in colour, and so successful were they that the old

Delftware (earthenware) bottles were driven from the market. By the 18th century the glass bottle had changed its shape to the now familiar tall cylinder, designed so that it could be 'laid down'.

Most collectable bottles were 'free-blown' (i.e. not moulded), and thus no two examples are identical. English bottles up to the early 19th century were prone to irregularities — particularly uneven bases, distorted necks and deformed glass seals — which, of course, collectors greatly savour.

Above: A 17th-century German armorial stoneware bottle, 10½in (26.25cm) high. £400.

Right: A treacle-glazed stoneware 'Irish Reform' cordial bottle depicting Daniel O'Connell, by Denby & Codnor, *c.* 1830, 7⅜in (19.5cm) high. £400.

Above: Amethyst-glass and white-glass apothecaries' bottles, early 19th century. £80-100.

Above, right: A 1940s Perrier bottle (for distribution in France). £5.

Right: A pre-World War I beer bottle. £15.

BUTTONS

In the early 16th century the previous devices used to fasten clothes (the toggle, brooch and lace) gave way to the button (often made by jewellers). In the 18th century, porcelain and linen buttons were made: the former are really objects of vertu, while hand-stitched 'wheel-pattern' and 'high-top' (conical) linen buttons, although not common, can still be found for up to £20.

The majority of buttons collected today are 19th century, and examples can be found in glass, enamel, bone and mother-of-pearl, as well as buttons covered in silk and linen. Uniform buttons also offer collecting potential. They were made in batches, and the appropriate size and number were taken to the tailor as required. Often they were fastened to clothing by split pins for easy removal during cleaning. So strongly were men's shirt cuffs starched in the 19th century that cuff-links evolved as a more practical alternative to the attached button.

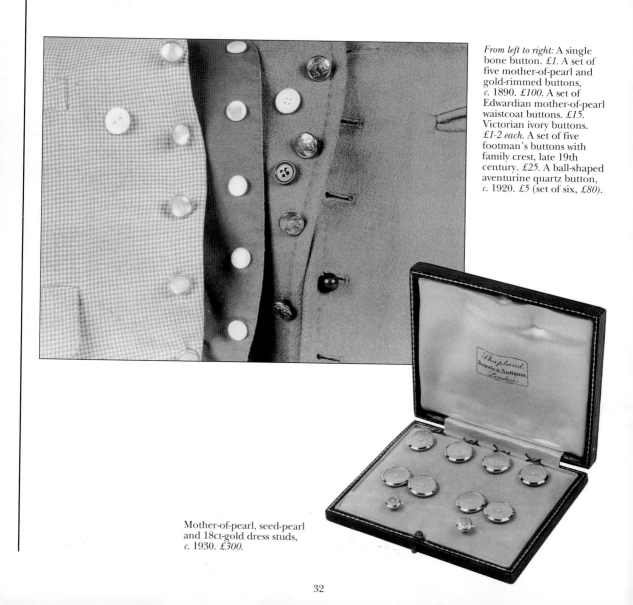

From left to right: A single bone button. *£1.* A set of five mother-of-pearl and gold-rimmed buttons, *c.* 1890. *£100.* A set of Edwardian mother-of-pearl waistcoat buttons. *£15.* Victorian ivory buttons. *£1-2 each.* A set of five footman's buttons with family crest, late 19th century. *£25.* A ball-shaped aventurine quartz button, *c.* 1920. *£5 (set of six, £80).*

Mother-of-pearl, seed-pearl and 18ct-gold dress studs, *c.* 1930. *£300.*

CARD CASES

Card cases became popular in the early 19th century and were used for the protection of visiting cards left by the 'polite' classes while calling on their neighbours and friends. They come in several distinct forms and sizes, some having small lids with tiny hinges, others having 'sleeve' lids that slide off completely, while others are modelled as books with a press-button catch which releases the two halves to reveal a kid-skin lining, often divided into compartments for cards and stamps. These may also be fitted with ivory aide-mémoires and tiny pencils.

Women's card cases tend to be larger than men's, presumably as they were carried in handbags rather than tight pockets. Men's also tend to be slimmer and plainer, often curved to fit in waistcoat pockets.

The earliest card cases date from the early 1800s and are simple in outline, but by the 1830s shaped and more elaborate designs became popular. Particularly collectable are the fine examples by Nathaniel Mills, especially his 'castle-tops', where celebrated and famous landmarks were cast in high relief, which can fetch up to £900.

As card cases became lighter most were decorated with bright-cut designs of flowers and foliage, each with a small cartouche for the initials of the owner. In the 1870s and 1880s 'aesthetic' cases with Japanese-style decoration became popular; such designs incorporated frosting, parcel gilding and engravings of birds and flowering peonies within fan-shaped panels. These can fetch between £300 and £350.

In the late 19th century, when card cases became increasingly used by the upper and middle classes, machine-rolled or engine-turned examples were often of a relatively poor quality and hardly worth their weight in silver, but those stamped with elaborate arabesques and cherubs can fetch up to £350.

Edwardian and later card cases reverted to simplicity, often with engine-turned decorations and perhaps fitted with suspensory chains so that they could be carried in the evenings. Novelty cases with revolving wheels that pushed one card up at a time also came into fashion.

Card cases were also made in ivory, tortoiseshell and mother-of-pearl, with or without silver mounts. With the advent of the telephone and changed social mores after World War I, they ceased to be manufactured.

A silver card case, rectangular with engraved foliate scrolls, engraved with initials within a shaped cartouche, Birmingham, 1906. £80.

A tortoiseshell card case. £60.

An ebony and ivory card case, rectangular form with pull-off cover, inlaid white-metal geometric decoration. £80.

Right: An Art Nouveau silver card case, rounded rectangular, the front chased with a female mask in a petal-shaped cartouche, Birmingham, 1901. £50-80.

Left: A Nathaniel Mills silver 'castle-top' card case, rectangular with hinged cover, engraved throughout with leaves and scrolls, the front showing the Crystal Palace and gardens, Birmingham, 1853. £550.

CERAMICS

Condition is one of the most important factors to look for when buying ceramics — not just for the obvious missing parts (such as handles or finials) but for any signs of restoration. The latter can decrease the value of a piece almost as much as breakage. To check bowls and plates for restoration, balance the piece on one hand, tap the side and listen for a clear ringing tone. If the sound is more of a thud, inspect the piece for colour variations and changes in texture. Key points for collectors are condition, rarity (not necessarily age) and quality of modelling and painted decoration. A useful guideline to follow when dating ceramics is that the 'England' mark was incorporated into all factory marks from 1891. Similarly, 'Made in England' is found only from 1901.

Hand-painted porcelain/pottery is of a far higher quality than printed ware. A transfer-printed flower is built up of dots, while a hand-painted flower is smooth and created by brushstrokes.

Some 19th-century blue-and-white tableware is collectable. Those patterns that were either unpopular or too complicated to produce, and hence were withdrawn from production, are now rare and keenly sought.

A Clarice Cliff jug, orange glazed, 9¼in (23.5cm) high. £40.

Above: A Clarice Cliff one-handed lotus jug, 11⅝in (29.5cm) high. £180.

Opposite: A Clarice Cliff 'fantasque' jardinière painted in the 'Melon' pattern in tones of yellow, green iron-red and puce above a wide band of orange edged in black, 8in (20.5cm) high. *£1,200.*

Above: A Clarice Cliff Bizarre plate, 1934, from the circus series designed by Dame Laura Knight, 9in (22.8cm) diam. *£650.*

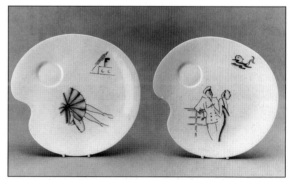

Above: A pair of Clarice Cliff Bizarre 'Cruiseware' plates, 11in (18cm) wide. *£30 each.*

Left: A Brannam Barum vase, with incised signature, 1905, 10⅜in (37.5cm) high. £150.

Below: A Charlotte Rhead Crown Ducal bowl, in orange and grey outlined with grey slip, 10in (25.5cm) diam. *£50.*

Above: A collection of Clarice Cliff domestic pieces including (from left to right) a Bizarre plate with 'Lightning' pattern, 'fantasque' biscuit barrel with 'Broth' pattern, conical sugar sifter in 'Honolulu' pattern, jug and basin in the 'Trees and House' pattern, jam pot with motifs, Lynton coffee service in the 'Coral Firs' pattern, conical bowl painted with the 'Gayday' pattern, and honey pot and cover in the 'Windbells' pattern. Prices range from £60 (sugar sifter) to £3,200 (Lynton coffee service).

Left: Part of a Clarice Cliff 'Appliqué' Bizarre coffee set, decorated in the 'Avignon' pattern, consisting of a conical coffee pot with triangular handle, a milk jug, a sugar bowl and six cups and saucers. £1,000.

Above, top: A Paragon bone china, two-handled loving cup commemorating the coronation of Edward VIII, 5in (13cm) high. *£480.*

Above, lower left: A Royal Doulton pottery beaker, titled 'Coronation H.M. King Edward VIII', 3½in (9cm) high. *£80.*

Above, lower right: A Staffordshire china mug commemorating the coronation of Edward VIII, after an original design by Dame Laura Knight, 3¼in (8cm) high. *£110.*

Above, left: A Staffordshire pottery child's plate, printed and overpainted with a full portrait of the young Queen Victoria, *c.* 1837, 7in (18cm) diam. *£100.*

Above, centre: A small blue-and-white Staffordshire pottery plate, printed with a head-and-shoulders portrait of the young Victoria, 3¼in (8.5cm) diam. *£90.*

Above, right: A Staffordshire pottery octagonal-sided child's plate, printed and painted with a half-portrait of the young Queen Victoria, 7in (18cm) diam. *£250.*

A Staffordshire pottery octagonal child's plate with a portrait of Queen Adelaide, *c.* 1830, 7¼in (8.5cm) diam. *£280.*

A Staffordshire pottery octagonal-sided child's daisy plate, printed in purple with a half-portrait of William IV wearing full military uniform, The Order of the Garter pinned to his jacket, titled in capitals 'William The Fourth, King of Great Britain', 7in (18cm) diam, *c.* 1830. *£230.*

Right: A Copeland 'subscriber's copy' cup commemorating the Transvaal War of 1899-1900, 5¼in (13.5cm) high. £1,050.

Left, top: A Royal Doulton earthenware cup commemorating the death of George V in 1936. £220.

Far left: A Harrods china mug commemorating the coronation of George V and Queen Mary in 1911. £100.

Left: A pottery mug commemorating the Silver Jubilee of George V and Queen Mary. £35.

Above, from left to right:
A Royal Doulton bone-china vase decorated by Charles Beresford Hopkins, 8⅝in (22cm) high. £400.

A Doulton Crown Lambeth faience vase designed by John Hassall, 7⅛in (18cm) high. £60.

A Royal Doulton Burslem bone-china vase decorated by Harry Nixon, 13in (33cm) high. £400.

A Royal Doulton pottery jar and cover designed by Reco Capey, 8¼in (21cm) high. £50.

A Royal Doulton stoneware vase designed by Mark V. Marshall, 8in (20cm) high. £120.

Above, left: An unusual Doulton Lambeth stoneware tobacco jar and cover, 7⅝in (19.5cm) high. £300.

Above, top: A rare Doulton Lambeth 'majolica' cachepot and stand, 8¼in (21cm) high. £250.

Above, right: A Doulton Lambeth stoneware jug, 12in (30.5cm) high. £180.

Above, bottom centre: A Doulton Burslem china tea kettle, 7⅞in (19.8cm) high (including handle). £100.

Below: One of a set of seven Crown Ducal plates, 8¼in (20.5cm) diam. *£100 the set.*

Above, left: A Doulton Lambeth grey stoneware lemonade jug with silver hinged cover, decorated by Hannah B. Barlow, the silver mounts and cover with London hallmarks for 1871, 10¼in (26cm) high. *£100.*

Above, top: A Doulton Lambeth stoneware vase, decorated by Hannah B. Barlow, 12½in (32cm) high. *£300.*

Above, right: A Royal Doulton stoneware vase, decorated by Hannah B. Barlow, 8in (20cm) high. *£200.*

Above, bottom centre: A Doulton Lambeth stoneware salad bowl with silver rim, decorated by Hannah B. Barlow, 8in (20cm) high. *£300.*

Left: A Doulton Lambeth stoneware roundel sculpted by George Tinworth, 9½in (24cm) diam. *£500.*

Right, from left to right:
A Doulton Lambeth faience vase, decorated by J.H. McLennan, 13½ in (34cm) high. *£400.*

One of a pair of Doulton Lambeth faience vases, 8in (20cm) high. *£50 each.*

A Doulton Lambeth faience vase painted by Katherine B. Smallfield. *£100.*

A Doulton Lambeth faience vase painted by Helen A. Arding, 11⅜in (22.5cm) high. *£200.*

A Doulton Crown Lambeth faience vase painted by Alice Marshall, 8⅜in (22.5cm) high. *£150.*

A Doulton Lambeth faience bottle vase, 8½in (22cm) high. *£50.*

A Doulton Lambeth faience vase decorated by Mary Butterton, 16½in (42cm) high. *£100.*

Far left and right: Part of a set of six Royal Doulton bone-china cabinet plates, 1927, painted by George Evans, 8¾in (22cm) diam. *£250 the set.*

Left, centre top: A Doulton Burslem luscian-ware vase painted by J. Hancock, 9½in (24cm) high. *£40.*

Left, centre bottom: A Doulton Lambeth stoneware bibelot, modelled in the form of a mouse, 3in (7.5cm). *£150.*

Above: Part of a Limoges tea set. *£100 the set.*

Above, right: A collection of Goss and crested china, including a Goss model of Joseph of Arimathea's church (*£700*) and an Edward VII memorial vase (*£50*). The other pieces sell for *£15-30 each.*

Right: A Goss model of the font in Winchester cathedral. *£350.*

Opposite page, top: A collection of Goss and crested-china pieces including a Cauldron China model of the Queen's dollshouse, *£60*; a Goss model of Shakespeare's house, *£120*, and a Goss model of the actress Ellen Terry's farmhouse, *£200*. The other pieces sell for *£15-30 each.*

Opposite page, top row of jugs: A superb pottery silver-lustre harlequin jug probably by Harley, *c.* 1815, 11½in (29cm) high, *£700.* A silver-lustre jug, 6⅝in (17cm), *£240.* A silver-lustre pottery jug, *£1,000.*

Opposite page, lower row of jugs: A small silver-lustre milk jug, 5¼in (13.5cm) high, *£250.* A silver-lustre milk jug, *c.* 1815, 5⅝in (14.5cm) high, *£130.* A silver-lustre milk jug, *c.* 1810, 5¼in (13.5cm) high, *£80.* A small silver-lustre milk jug, 5½in (14cm) high, *£250.*

Above, top row from left to right: A pink teacup and saucer of 'Bute' shape, *£25.* A pink-lustre Leeds-type finger vase, *c.* 1815, 8½in (21.5cm) high, *£180.* A silver-lustre milk jug, *c.* 1810, 5⅝in (14.5cm) high, *£150.*

Above, centre: A pink-lustre and puce printed milk jug, 3½in (9cm) high, *£40.*

Above, bottom row, from left to right: A pink-lustre Leeds-type teapot, *c.* 1820, 6in (15cm) high, *£120.* A miniature pink-lustre jug, 3in (7.5cm) high, *£55.* An English porcelain teapot and cover, *c.* 1815, 6½in (16.5cm) high, *£130.*

Top left: A copper-lustre two-handled flared vessel with cover, *c.* 1880, 11in (28cm) high. £80.

Top right: A copper-lustre coffee pot and cover, *c.* 1815, 11½in (29cm) high. £170.

Centre: A copper-lustre goblet, *c.* 1835, 4¼in (11cm) high. £60-70.

Bottom left: A farmer's lustre mug, *c.* 1825, 5½in (14cm) high. £250.

Bottom centre: A canary copper-lustre milk jug, *c.* 1810, 5in (12.5cm) high. £260.

Lower right: A copper-lustre waisted cylindrical mug, *c.* 1830, 3in (7.5cm) high. £40.

Right-hand corner: One of a pair of salts, *c.* 1825, 2¼in (5.5cm) high. £85 *the pair.*

Above: MARTINWARE
Top centre: A stoneware jug,
4⅝in (12cm) high. *£350.*

Top right: A stoneware
spoonwarmer, 5in (12.5cm)
high. *£800.*

Lower left: A stoneware vase,
7½in (19cm) high. *£400.*

Lower centre and right: Two
stoneware cachepots, 4½in
(11.5cm) high. *£950 each.*

Right: A Copeland Parian
bust, modelled as 'The
Veiled Bride', *c.* 1860, 14½in
(37cm) high. *£750.*

Left: A Poole pottery vase, 9⅞in (25cm) high. *£50.*

Right: A Poole pottery shagreen vase, 10½in (27cm) high. *£160.*

Left: Two pot-lids with 'activity' subjects: *Above:* A medium-size pot-lid depicting 'The Enthusiast', a popular subject after a painting by Theodore Lane. *£30-40. Below:* A small lid showing 'Bears at School'. *£40-60.*

Right: Two large scenic pot-lids: *Above:* A framed pot-lid depicting 'Strasbourg', probably used for a Crosse and Blackwell's paste-pot. *£50-80. Below:* A framed pot-lid, illustrating 'The Picnic', with fancy border and Jesse Austin's initials on the left. *£50-80.*

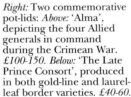

Left: 'The Village Wedding', a common lid registered by F. & R. Pratt in 1857, after a painting by Teniers. *£30-40.*

Right: Two commemorative pot-lids: *Above:* 'Alma', depicting the four Allied generals in command during the Crimean War. *£100-150. Below:* 'The Late Prince Consort', produced in both gold-line and laurel-leaf border varieties. *£40-60.*

Left: 'Dr Johnson', another common subject, which depicts Dr Johnson waiting to see Lord Chesterfield. *£30-40.*

Below: A Ruskin pottery vase, 10¼in (26cm) high. £80.

Above: Two pot-lids with dog subjects: *Top:* 'The Snow Drift', adapted from the painting 'The Rescue' by Sir Edwin Landseer. *£30-50.* *Bottom:* 'Low Life', adapted from Landseer's painting of the same title. *£30-50.*

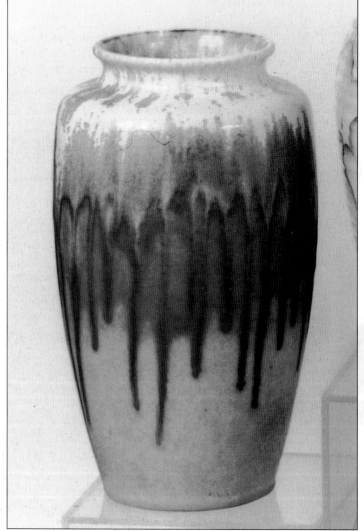

Right: A Shelley vase garniture, signed by Walter Slater, 8¼in (21cm) high. *£100.*

Below: A titled pair of Staffordshire portrait figures, *c.* 1836, depicting Edward Morgan and Jenny Jones, 11⅜in (29cm) and 10⅛in (25.7cm) high respectively. *£1,000.*

Above left: A Staffordshire figure, *c.* 1854, of General Sir Colin Campbell, 12in (30.5cm) high. *£480.*

Above, centre: Staffordshire: a well-coloured group of an English sailor and French soldier, *c.* 1854, 13½in (33cm) high. *£550.*

Above right: Staffordshire: 'The Wounded Soldier', *c.* 1855, 10½in (16.5cm) high. *£190.*

Staffordshire: 'The Victory', depicting an English sailor, *c.* 1856, 14¼in (36.25cm) high. *£700.*

Staffordshire: a rare model of Florence Nightingale, *c.* 1855, 10½in (26.5cm) high. *£900.*

Above, left: Staffordshire: a spill vase, *c.* 1850, possibly depicting Lady Hester Stanhope, 13in (33cm) high. *£180.*

Above, centre: Staffordshire: a well-coloured model of a cavalier and his female companion, 16in (41cm) high. *£150.*

Above, right: A model of a pair of musicians, *c.* 1855, 13in (33cm) high. *£150.*

Left: A Susie Cooper coffee jug, painted in green below a broad grey band. *£50.*

Above, Toby jugs from left to right:
A Staffordshire sailor, *c.* 1780, 11⅜in (29cm) high. *£1,700.*

A creamware Admiral Lord Howe, *c.* 1780, 9½in (24cm) high. *£1,600.*

A Davenport 'Martha Gunn', 1836, 12½in (32cm) high. *£750.*

A Walton 'Hearty Good Fellow', *c.* 1810, 11in (28cm) high. *£1,000.*

A Yorkshire-type jug, *c.* 1800, 9½in (24cm) high. *£400.*

Left: A rare silver-lustre 'King Hal' Toby jug, *c.* 1820, 15in (38cm) high. *£3,000.*

Above: A collection of
Wemyss-ware. *£100-120 each.*

A large Wemyss-ware three-
handled loving cup, 9½in
(24cm) high. *£500.*

A cut-cornered rectangular
Wemyss-ware tray, 10in
(25.5cm) wide. *£200.*

Left: A Wemyss-ware jardinière, 8in (20cm) high. *£400.*

Below: A Wilkinson's Bizarre lotus jug, 11in (28cm) high. *£200.*

Left: A Worcester majolica teapot in the Chinese style, 9¼in (23.5cm) high. *£200.*

Right: Three modern bowls by Tessa Fuchs. *£60-110 each.*

Above: Three modern vases by Adam Sutherland. *£100-130 each.*

Above: Three modern pieces by Andrew Watford. *Left to right:* a stoneware vase, 17¾in (45cm) high, *£260.* A stoneware vase, 5½in (14cm) high, *£50.* A stoneware charger, 16¾in (43cm) diam, *£140.*

Above, left: A modern bowl on drum by Gordon Baldwin, 8⅝in (22cm) high. *£160.*

Above, centre: A modern stoneware salt-glazed jug by Walter Keeler, 7½in (19cm) high. *£160.*

Above, right: A modern stoneware bowl sculpture by Gordon Baldwin, 13⅓in (34cm) diam. *£150.*

Right: A modern bowl, 18in (46cm) diam, and (*far right*) a stoneware plate, 15¼in (39cm) diam by Rupert Spira. Bowl: *£380.* Plate: *£160.*

Right, from left to right: A modern moulded porcelain dish by Jacqueline Poncelet, 13¾in (34.5cm) high, *£100.* A porcelain vase by Mary Rich, 15in (38cm) high, *£120.* A porcelain bowl by Mary Rich, 11⅜in (29cm) high, *£120.*

Above left: A modern raku sculpture by Rosa Nguyen, 18⅛in (47cm) high. *£300.*

Above right: A modern ceramic pot by Peter Hayes, 21in (52.5cm) high. *£320.*

Three modern stoneware pieces by Bernard Rooke. *£100-150 each.*

CLOCKS

Clocks are popular with collectors for their decorative appeal as well as technical interest. Those clocks most in demand date from the 17th, 18th and 19th centuries. Earlier clocks are very rare and are poor time-keepers, thus they tend to be appreciated for their furniture value only.

Examples made by members of the Clock Makers' Company in London in the early 18th century are the most sought-after and command high prices. Lower prices are realised by provincial clocks, as these tend to be less in demand, but they still make good decorative pieces. Clocks made by master clockmakers such as Daniel Quare, George Graham and Thomas Tompion are the most valuable.

The styles of long-case clocks reflect those of the furniture of the time, for example the cases of late 17th-century long-case clocks are usually made of oak, veneered with ebony or walnut and decorated with floral marquetry.

Due to wear with use, clock movements are rarely in their original condition. The escapement wears out particularly quickly and, without replacing it, the clock would not function. High prices are commanded where the case, dial and cast ornaments are in original condition. It is totally acceptable for the escapement to have been replaced, but the movement should be otherwise untouched.

Below, left: A French Empire ormolu mantel clock of vase form, signed 'Tarault à Paris, St. Honoré No. 24', moon hands, white enamel dial, the handles are formed as swan necks above masks of Bacchus, on square base, 15½in (39cm). £800.

Below, right: A French Empire mantel timepiece, the drum supported within a lyre above swans, on an oval bronze base with ormolu mounts, 13in (33cm). £300.

Above, left: An early Victorian mahogany striking mantel clock, 5in (12.5cm) silvered dial with foliate engraved spandrels, two-train fusée movement with anchor escapement, pull repeating on a gong, in a moulded architectural case with horizontal flutes and carved foliate decoration to the door and base, 10½in (27cm). £650.

Above, right: A mahogany four-glass mantel timepiece, 4in (10cm) silvered dial with scroll engraved spandrels, the single-train fusée movement with anchor escapement, in a moulded case with glazed sides and top, 9in (23cm). £480.

Below, left: A Victorian ebonised quarter chiming bracket clock and bracket, 7½in brass dial, signed 'J. W. Benson, Ludgate Hill', twin subsidiaries for slow/fast and chime/silent, the three-train fusée movement with signed backplate, chiming on gongs, in a moulded bell-top case flanked by gilt-brass mounts caryatids, torch finials, 29in (73cm). £950.

Below, right: A late Victorian quarter-chiming ebonised mantel clock, the 7½in (19cm) silvered circular dial with chime/silent lever at 9 o'clock and four bells/eight bells at 3 o'clock, the three-train fusée movement with eight-bell carillon backplate, in an arched case with gilt-metal mounts, urn finials, 20½in (52cm). £580.

Opposite, from left to right: A French four-glass mantel clock, circular white enamel dial, the two-train movement with mercury pendulum, in a moulded serpentine case, on bun feet, 10½in (27cm). £380.

A French four-glass mantel clock of large size, signed on the square-plated movement and white enamel dial 'Ambrosoni, Paris', visible Brocot escapement, gridiron pendulum, in a very substantial moulded case with bevelled glass and enamelled degree arc in the base, 19in (49cm). £950.

A French four-glass mantel clock, two-train movement with mercury pendulum, the gilt dial signed 'Mappin & Webb', in a moulded case, the pediment and base with bands of beading, 11in (28cm). £320.

Far left: A mahogany striking bracket clock, the 8in (20cm) painted dial signed 'Henry Harris, London', between the slow/fast and strike/silent subsidiaries, the two-train movement with engraved border signed 'Robson, Cripplegate, London', in a break-arch case stamped in the back 'Robson, No. 1381', the panelled top with carrying handle, 17in (43cm). £1,350.

Left: An ebony veneered striking verge bracket clock, 7in (17.5cm) circular white enamel dial, two-train movement signed on the backplate 'William Story, London', in a break-arch case with brass-bound triple-pad top surmounted by carrying handle, 13in (33cm), *c.* 1780. £2,100.

Above, left: A mahogany balloon bracket clock, the 8in (20cm) white painted dial signed 'James Upjohn, London', strike/silent lever at 3 o'clock, two-train fusée movement with engraved border to the signed backplate, in a waisted case painted with flowers and musical trophies, torch finial, ogee feet, 25in (63cm). £850.

Above, right: A Regency mahogany striking bracket clock, the 8in (20cm) convex painted dial signed 'Barrand, Cornhill, London', the circular plated two-train movement with engraved border and signed within a cartouche, in a lancet case with ebonised stringing and brass inlay, 20in (51cm). £1,200.

Above: A white-metal mantel clock, after a design by Otto Prutscher, the lozenge-shaped dial decorated with a petal motif and set with four cabochons, the matching pendulum enclosed within a glass casing, mounted on six cylindrical feet, on streaked marble base, 14⅜in (36.5cm). £10,000–15,000.

Above, left to right:
A small silver travelling timepiece, circular white enamel dial, eight-day carriage-type movement with lever escapement, signed on the brass backplate 'Cartier No. 170', in a rectangular silver case with gold bezel, 2½in (6.5cm), London, 1920, with tooled green leather travelling case. *£600.*

A decorative grande sonnerie and alarum carriage clock, the ivory dial painted with doves amongst flowers, pierced and engraved foliate mask to the surround, signed 'John Mason, Paris', in a serpentine case flanked by fluted columns with acanthus capitals, the strike selection lever in the base, 5½in (14cm). *£1,200.*

A gorge-cased alarum carriage clock of small size, white enamel dial with subsidiary alarum dial beneath, the repeating movement with lever platform, the back numbered 8553 and signed 'repassée par Leroy & Fils, Palais Royal, Paris', in a moulded gorge case, 4½in (11.5cm). *£750.*

Left: A late Victorian quarter-chiming mahogany mantel clock, the 5in (12.5 cm) brass dial signed 'Lund & Blockley, To the Queen, Pall Mall, London', chime/silent in the arch, eight bells/four bells lever at 3 o'clock, the three-train fusée movement chiming on eight bells and four gongs, in a bell-top case with brass inlaid fluted canted corners, brass bands and pineapple finials, 17in (43cm). *£1,700.*

COSTUME

Clothing reflects social as well as purely fashion trends. An example is how the restrictive clothes worn by many Victorian and Edwardian women gave way to much looser dress in the wake of woman's suffrage and World War I. One of the great charms of collecting costume is that there is always a connection to a particular wearer, and the enthusiast can imagine the circumstances and history of its original owner.

The market for collectable costume also extends to accessories such as hats, gloves, handbags, scarves and shoes. Indeed, many collectors prefer them because they are much easier to display. Whatever your particular interest, buy clothes and accessories in the best possible condition you can. Avoid torn, faded and mildewed garments, and remember that alteration or restoration may greatly reduce value. Clothes from well-known designers and couturiers – even as late as the 1970s – command high prices.

Above: An Edwardian cream satin evening or presentation dress, the heavily beaded bodice and skirt overlaid with needlerun lace, and later petrol-blue satin skirt and fur-lined cape embroidered with metal thread, the cape lined with pale coral velvet. *£100–150.*

Right: A rare Pacquin pale aquamarine silk, lace and chiffon gown trimmed with silk toggles and a bow decorating the high waistband, labelled 'Pacquin, Paris-London', *c. 1910. £300–500.*

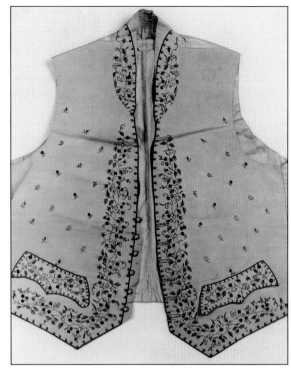

Above: A Chinese robe of midnight-blue silk embroidered with baskets of flowers and butterflies, the wide sleeve bands embroidered with large flowerheads, some in Peking knot, on an ivory ground. £150–250.

Below: A chasuble front of ivory silk heavily embroidered with metal thread and coloured silk in an overall design of 'C'-scrolls, rambling vines and large flowerheads, French, *c.* mid-18th century. £200–300.

Above: A mid-19th century gentleman's grosgrain silk waistcoat, embroidered with trailing flowers in various coloured silk threads. £100–150.

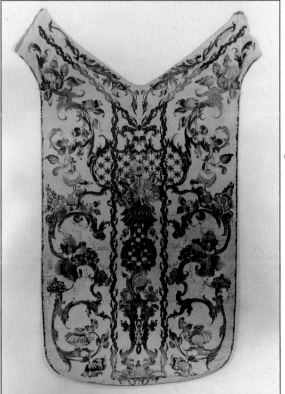

Left: A Victorian country wedding dress of gold silk, the bodice, cuffs and bustle skirt trimmed with small pleats, zig-zag borders and rosettes, *c.* 1875. £100–200.

CYCLING

Collectable bicycles start with the 'Penny Farthing', invented in 1818, which can cost up to £1,000, according to age and condition. A solid-tyred chain-driven tricycle of the late 1880s may cost £4,000, and a 'bone-shaker' £2,000.

Prices vary considerably for bicycles of this period, according to age, condition and the accessories they carry. The invention of chain-driven machines (1885) and the pneumatic tyre (1892) revolutionised cycling. Given prices like these for veteran machines, it is hardly surprising that early 20th-century bicycles have risen in price. One can pay £200 for a 1920s Raleigh, and there is a growing market for associated memorabilia: lamps, cyclometers, panniers and the like.

Clockwise, from top:
A Raleigh 'X'-frame bicycle, *c.* 1890. *£200.*

A late 1930s grocer's delivery tricycle with replacement box. *£700.*

A Thompson's automatic cyclometer, with chromed body and enamelled face bearing four dials, *c.* 1877. *£50.*

A 1937 James tricycle. *£300.*

DRINKING BYGONES

Luckily, many of the bygones associated with drinking are as useful as they are attractive. Drinking glasses, decanters, silver wine labels and coasters are among those which represent the upper end of the market, while commemorative bottles of beer, beer mats and towels and other pub memorabilia are examples of the inexpensive end.

Old drinking glasses, whether for wine or ale, need not be expensive. Many beautiful rummers and half-ales can be found for under £100 (although an 18th-century glass like that on page 74 will command a great deal more).

Decanters (once essential due to the high level of sediment in 19th-century wine) are now once again in demand. The Victorian and Edwardian tantalus (three decanters in a lockable wood and metal cabinet/frame) is particularly sought-after, and a good one will cost about £500.

The newest area of drinking collectables is pub memorabilia, and is mainly concerned with advertising bygones such as ashtrays and bar jugs — a good selection of which can be found under Advertising on page 11.

Above, from left to right:
A silver-mounted claret jug, cut-glass body on a circular foot, leaf-engraved scroll handle and engraved collar and cover with finial, London, 1900, 10⅓in (26.25cm) high. *£480.*

A Victorian claret jug, the body with loop handle, plain silver collar and domed hinged cover, with monogram engraved to centre, London, 1890, 8in (20cm) high. *£300.*

A Victorian claret jug, oval hobnail cut-glass body, reeded angled handle, the collar chased with ovals of floral clusters and stylised leaves, the fluted hinged cover with beaded borders and pierced thumbpiece, Sheffield, 1871, by the Sissons Brothers, 9¾in (24.8cm) high. *£700.*

Right: A good early Victorian wine-cooler, the slightly domed lid enclosing a lead-lined interior, on moulded 'C'-scroll feet, 31in (78.5cm) wide, stamped. *£950.*

Right: A pair of George III wine labels, octagonal with reeded borders, London, 1807, by Elizabeth Morley. *£60.*

Far right: A matched set of three wine labels, octagonal with reeded borders, *top* London, 1806, by Phipps and Robinson, *middle* London, 1804, by Phipps and Robinson, *bottom* Edinburgh, 1911, by Hamilton and Inches. *£120.*

Below: A set of three drinks labels, with engraved scroll and fruiting vine decoration, Birmingham, 1839, by George Unite. *£170.*

Above: A pair of Georgian lacquered papier-mâché wine coasters, the sides gilded with scrolling acanthus leaves and vine fruits, 5⅓in (14cm) diam. *£280.*

Above: A set of four cut-glass cordial decanters without stoppers, of cylindrical form with knopped and faceted circular necks above sloping faceted shoulders, the sides engraved with 'Shrub', 'Mint', 'Raspberry' and 'Lovage' 11¼in (28.5cm) high. *£360.*

Right: One of a pair of decanters, etched with floral swags and with a fluted neck, chased-silver mount, the neck mount with hinged cover and topped by a cast female figure, import mark for Chester, 1900, by Bertholdt Müller, 11in (28cm) high. *£1,150.*

Left: A Victorian claret jug, the baluster-form glass body etched with bands of stylised anthemions, leaves and Greek key pattern, the domed hinged cover chased with vines and flowers, Sheffield, 1889, by W. & F. Sissons, 10in (25cm) high. *£1,200.*

Above: William Comyns. A set of four silver-gilt mounted decanters, the rectangular bottles with applied silver-gilt mounts pierced and chased with latticework, flowers and scrolls, the domed hinged covers with push-button release, chased with figures within a classical setting revealing drop stoppers, London, 1903, 7½in (9cm) high. *£2,200.*

Right: A Victorian carved-oak tantalus, with three cut-glass decanters and stoppers, twin hinged doors opening to reveal compartments, bound in cast-iron, with twin handles, 14in (35.5cm) wide. *£500.*

FANS

Initially developed to keep people cool, fans gradually took on ceremonial and religious roles and became status symbols. There are three main types — fixed, brisé and folding.

The fixed fan (rigid and with a handle) is common in the Orient, for example the Chinese *pien mien* which is made from paper stretched over a wire frame and then decorated.

Brisé fans (produced in Europe and the East) are made mainly from sticks of ivory, wood and bamboo and are often intricately carved. These sticks, or 'slips', are held together at the base by a cord or a rivet, using thread or ribbon further up the fan. It was not until the early 17th century that heavy end-sticks, or 'guards', were used in brisé fans.

The folding fan is a further development of the brisé fan, attaching a 'leaf' to the sticks in imitation of a batwing. The leaf is often decorated with patterns or scenes and can be made from several different types of material, for example paper, fabric, lace and fine skins. Additional ornamentation, such as mother-of-pearl inlay, decorated the guards.

When buying fans expect to pay more for examples in good condition with high-quality decoration, particularly if painted by an artist of renown. Famous previous owners also make a difference to the value, but ensure that there is written validation.

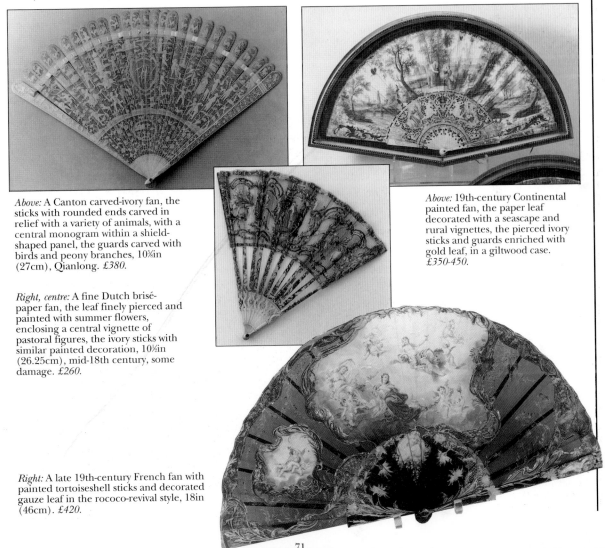

Above: A Canton carved-ivory fan, the sticks with rounded ends carved in relief with a variety of animals, with a central monogram within a shield-shaped panel, the guards carved with birds and peony branches, 10⅝in (27cm), Qianlong. £380.

Right, centre: A fine Dutch brisé-paper fan, the leaf finely pierced and painted with summer flowers, enclosing a central vignette of pastoral figures, the ivory sticks with similar painted decoration, 10⅓in (26.25cm), mid-18th century, some damage. £260.

Above: 19th-century Continental painted fan, the paper leaf decorated with a seascape and rural vignettes, the pierced ivory sticks and guards enriched with gold leaf, in a giltwood case. £350-450.

Right: A late 19th-century French fan with painted tortoiseshell sticks and decorated gauze leaf in the rococo-revival style, 18in (46cm). £420.

FIRESIDE COLLECTABLES

As the fireplace formed an integral part of a room's decor, its style (and that of its attendant accessories) reflected the prevalent tastes in interior design. For example, Minton produced Arts & Craft-style tiles for fireplaces at the turn of the 19th century.

Fire surrounds (generally of marble, wood, cast-iron, slate or tile) reflected the importance of the house. Owners of grand houses often employed master stonemasons to create sculptural surrounds, while the Victorian and Edwardian speculative builder installed mass-produced examples.

Firescreens (usually of carved wood or tapestry) covered the openings of fires when they were not in use. Fenders (to prevent hot coals falling into the room), coal buckets and fire-irons (usually brass) were all part of the necessary equipment for an open fire.

During the 1920s and 1930s many fireplaces were modernised with Art Deco-style electric fires, and these are now keenly collected. Indeed the nostalgia boom of the 1980s has brought the fireplace and its related furniture very much back to life.

Above: An Art Deco cast-iron radiator cover, of rectangular section, the trelliswork embellished with gilt-metal beads, enclosing an octagonal panel with a flower basket, covered by a marble plaque, 36¾ x 40½in (93.5 x 103cm). *£400-600.*

Right, from top:
An early 19th-century japanned-metal coal bucket and cover, the foot, body and cover painted with gilt foliate swags on a black ground, the sides with twin handles, 23⅛in (59.5cm) high. *£250.*

A George III brass bowed fender, the pierced front engraved with a running stylised floral design, 61⅛in (156cm) wide. *£380.*

A set of three George III polished steel fire irons with pierced shovel. *£110.*

Below: A 19th-century gilt-bronze fender, the ends cast with figures of dogs on fluted concave plinths, 69in (175cm) long when fully extended. *£600.*

Right: A 1950s Lincoln Model F3 electric radiator, double heating element in front of curved polished metal reflector, covered at the front by V-shaped discs, on irregular-shaped metal base, 14in (35.5cm) wide. *£200.*

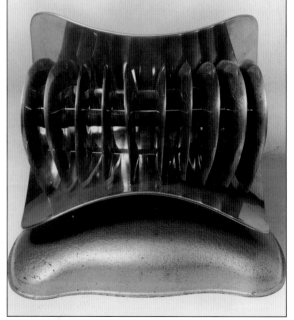

Above: George III Adam-style green painted pine and gesso fire surround, 74in (188cm) wide overall. *£800.*

Left:
Fire surround. George III-style pine and gesso, the frieze decorated with ribbon-tied husk chains, rosettes and centred by a classical medallion, 61in (155cm) outer dimension. *£1,000.*

Grate. A Louis XV style, steel and brass basket grate, the serpentine front on well-cast scroll supports, and volutes, 24in (61cm) wide. *£300.*

Fender. Victorian brass with a pierced oak-leaf pattern frieze and rounded ends on paw feet, 35½ in (90cm) wide. *£2,000.*

Irons. A matched set of four brass fire implements – shovel, tongs, poker and toasting fork. *£50.*

Right: A mid-19th-century French Carrara marble fire surround, the mantel with bevelled edge, carved scroll jams, paw feet, 52in (132cm) wide. *£1,000.*

Above: A William IV rosewood fire screen, the tapestry panel within a baluster-turned frame, on downcurved feet. *£250.*

Left: A rare early Victorian papier-mâché fire screen/occasional table, the rising hinged circular top decorated with priests in the interior of an abbey, on a spreading triform column, concave plinth with overscrolled feet, 20in (51cm) diam. *£900.*

GLASS

Glass has been produced since antiquity: the Egyptians, Syrians and Romans were all expert glass-workers. It can be 'blown' or moulded into any number of shapes, and can be coloured or made opaque by using metallic oxides. It is usually blown into a mould and then finished by hand. Sometimes it is decorated, either by painting with enamels and lacquer colours, or by etching and engraving. A popular 19th-century form of decoration was 'flashing', whereby clear glass was covered with a layer of coloured glass through which patterns were cut to reveal the clear glass. Early varieties of clear glass contain many impurities which result in slight discoloration (usually blue, green or yellow tones). If the glass is free of such impurities, it is probably modern.

Right: A Jacobite goblet, *c.* 1750, with portrait of Bonnie Prince Charlie, 8in (20cm) high. *£1,000.*

Bottom right: A Bohemian-style cranberry-glass comport painted with roses, *c.* 1900, 6½in (16.25cm) high. *£65.*

Below: Monart glass vase, 8in (20cm). *£100.*

Left: A Victorian white-overlay glass bonbonnière, 7in (17.5cm) high. *£50.*

Above: A Portuguese Bohemian-style flashed claret decanter, *c.* 1900, 10in (25cm) high. *£30.*

Left: Monart glass vase, 6in (15cm) high. *£60.*

Below: A large Victorian glass vase with milk ground ornately decorated with wild flowers, 23½in (59cm) high. *£1,000.*

Above: A 19th-century Bohemian glass vase, 16½in (42cm) high. *£700.*

Lalique. 'Sophora', a clear
grey-stained vase, moulded
with winding stems of heart-
shaped leaves, 10⅛in
(25.8cm) high. £2,600.

Lalique. 'Aras', a frosted
and sienna-stained vase,
moulded with crested
parakeets, 9in (23cm) high.
£2,100.

Lalique. 'Borneo', a clear,
frosted black enamelled
vase, moulded with birds
heightened in enamel, 9¼in
(23.5cm) high. £1,500.

Lalique. 'Roscoff', a clear
blue-stained dish, the
underside moulded with
radiating fish, the centre
with a myriad of bubbles,
14⅛in (36cm) diam. £900.

Lalique. 'Anges', an
opalescent and sienna-
stained dish, moulded in
intaglio with facing pairs of
kneeling angels, 14½in
(37cm) diam. £3,100.

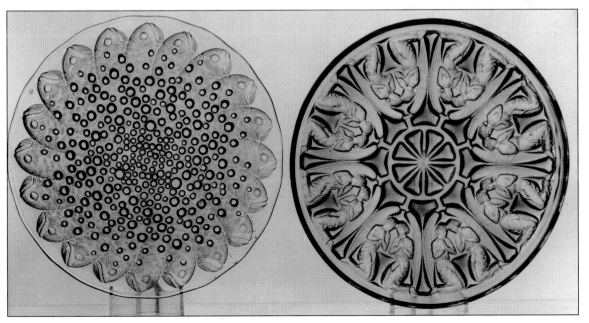

GRAMOPHONES

The predecessor of the gramophone was the phonograph, a clockwork-driven machine that played a foil or wax cylinder amplified through a metal horn. The phonograph was patented by Thomas Edison in 1878 and was initially marketed in the USA as a diction machine; it was not until Emile Berliner's work on disc pressing in 1888, the introduction of musical recording in the 1890s and the production of commercial cylinders from 1901, that it evolved into a machine of entertainment.

Early gramophones were manufactured by several companies, including the 'Vickers' made by Eldridge R. Johnson in England. Competition between manufacturers led to a rapid improvement in sound reproduction as well as the decorative aspects of the machines (gramophones were often housed in attractive wooden cabinets and are now collected as much for their visual appeal as their technical interest). Portable machines were introduced in 1914 by Barnett-Samuel of London, and their compactness makes them of special interest to the collector.

Right: A 1940s Columbia gramophone. *£30.*

Below: A Robeyphone Grand gramophone with green flower horn, *c.* 1912, 36in (90cm) high. *£300.*

INKWELLS

The earliest known vessel used to hold ink was the medieval cowhorn — waterproof and plentiful. And although pots and bowls were also subsequently used, the term 'inkhorn' survived into the 19th century to describe a portable inkwell. As literacy increased among the land-owning classes during the 16th century so did the proliferation of inkwells, and by the 17th century the screw-top well was firmly established. The 'standish' (a desk-stand incorporating a well, pen stand, water box and sometimes a taper stick) was commonplace by the 18th century.

Price is largely dictated by material — ormolu, porcelain, pewter, glass and precious metals, for example — but it is possible to put together a good collection of pieces costing on average less than £100 each (a 19th-century Staffordshire pottery inkwell may cost as much as £300, but on the other hand a common glass well with metal cap can be found for £10-15).

During the early 20th century the inkwell gave way to the ink bottle, and such bottles (like the one illustrated here) are also collectable.

Above: A late-1940s Pelikan reservoir inkbottle. *£50.*

Left: An early 19th-century ormolu and tortoiseshell standish. *£300-400.*

Below, left: A silver capstan inkwell, Birmingham, 1920. *£70.*

Below, right: A 1930s china inkwell with polychrome decoration. *£30*

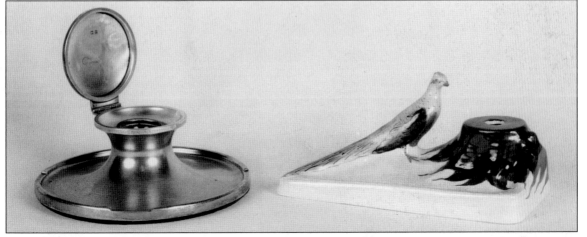

JEWELLERY

For many would-be collectors the nagging worry is whether a piece is genuine or not. Looking at jewellery in museums, auctions and dealers (as well as reading on the subject) will help, but it is also useful to have a x10 magnifying glass to help detect faults or repairs. The novice collector should always search out a dealer of repute.

The 19th and early 20th centuries are the richest for collectors, and the jewellers of that period worked with a wide variety of materials — jet, coral, cut steel, amber, agate and amethyst among them.

Costume jewellery appeared in quantity in the 19th century, and many of the pieces, set in pinchbeck or silver, are of a quality which would not shame the jewellery they were intended to imitate. If the piece is well designed, the novice collector is unlikely to get burned fingers.

Designer costume jewellery of the 20th century is rapidly growing in popularity. Here, the all-important factors are good strong style combined with a designer's name.

Far left: An Art Nouveau Continental white-metal pendant with two garnets. *£150.*

Left, from top: A Liberty & Co. silver and enamel Art Nouveau money clip, Birmingham hallmarks for 1904. *£200.*

A Liberty & Co. enamelled white-metal Art Nouveau brooch, attributed to a design by Jessie M. King. *£250.*

A French pliqué-à-jour and white-metal Art Nouveau wings brooch, the three sections inset with turquoise pliqué-à-jour wings enclosing a mother-of-pearl roundel. *£60.*

Opposite, top row left to right: A Victorian Celtic-style yellow-gold and freshwater-pearl cross pendant. *£190.*

A split-pearl and aquamarine necklace mounted in 15 ct. gold. *£420.*

A Victorian amethyst split-pearl and demantoid garnet brooch. *£270.*

A late-Victorian 18 ct. yellow-gold split-pearl and diamond brooch. *£350.*

Opposite, middle rows: An Edwardian opal necklet. *£740.*

An Edwardian amethyst pendant necklace. *£320.*

Above, bottom group from left to right:
An unusual mixed-metal brooch by Frederick James and May Hart Partridge, 1910. *£550.*

A Victorian diamond 'hawk' brooch, the body pavé set with rose-cut diamonds, cabochon ruby eyes, standing on a yellow-gold branch. *£1,350.*

A lozenge-shaped almandine garnet brooch, the garnets set with rose-cut diamond points, with a pearl fringe. *£600.*

An opal and diamond-cluster ring. *£600.*

A Victorian cabochon garnet and diamond brooch. *£220.*

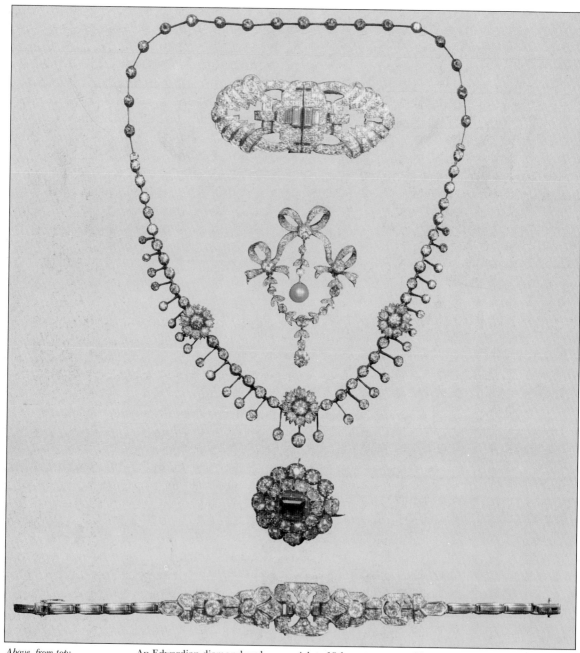

Above, from top:
A 1940s diamond and baguette-cut diamond double-clip brooch. *£1,500.*

An Edwardian diamond and pearl necklet: with platinum trace-link chain. *£800.*

A late-19th century diamond and rose-cut diamond fringe and cluster necklace tiara. *£2,000.*

A late 19th-century emerald and diamond brooch, the stones mounted in silver and gold. *£2,500.*

An Art Deco diamond bracelet with an expandable back bracelet. *£1,000.*

Above:
A French Art Nouveau black opal pendant, signed 'Arnould', *c.* 1900. *£1,200.*

Right:
An unusual Art Deco lapis lazuli and silver necklace with a diamond hinged cover revealing a watch, *c.* 1929. *£2,800.*

Right, from left to right:
A Lalique frosted grey-stained perfume pendant. *£3,200.*

A Lalique black opaque pendant. *£1,000.*

A Lalique blue bracelet. *£1,000.*

A Lalique sienna-stained and clear-glass pendant. *£1,000.*

A Lalique necklace composed of seven opaque black-glass spheres. *£1,500.*

JUKEBOXES

The Regina Corona of 1898 was an early music-box to play a selected tune, and by 1905 the Regina Automatic Reginaphone could offer a selection of six music-cylinders, with a horn to amplify the sound. Indeed, these machines were so successful they were able to hold their own against the phonograph for many years.

The 1920s saw the development of the jukebox by predominantly American companies — Rockola, Wurlitzer, Seeburg and AMI (Automatic Musical Instruments), for example — who exploited the new technology of electrical recording and amplification systems.

It is important to buy a machine from a reputable dealer who can give a guarantee that the model contains the original manufacturer's parts. Restoration is quite common (a good dealer can recommend a restorer) and will not unduly depress the value of the machine as long as the appropriate parts have been used.

Above: A Wurlitzer 'Model 1015' jukebox, *c.* 1946, the domed case with 24-button record selector to the front mounted above three coin chutes and chromed-metal grill, with Jacobs lightweight tone arm, for 78rpm, 59in (150cm) high. £6,500.

Left: A Mill's Empress jukebox, c. 1939, the rectangular wood case with rounded edges, framed by green and orange light panels, 20-button selector, and five, ten and 25 cent coin chute above a speaker unit covered in gold material behind gold-painted stylised foliate central strut, 59in (150cm) high. £2,500.

Below: A Chantal Meteor 200 jukebox, English, 1950s, the domed circular perspex case containing complete record list, framed to the front by a chromed-metal grill, upon tapering blue metal base with chrome grill and two tapering wooden legs, with 200-selection dial and 6d. coin chute to the front, 59in (150cm) high. £5,000.

Opposite, right: A Rockola '1428' jukebox, c. 1948, serial No. 115426, the domed front with 20-button record selector beside three coin chutes above a wooden fretwork grill, framed by green and red moulded light panels, 61in (154cm) high. £4,200.

KITCHENALIA

It is only in recent years that people have been interested in collecting kitchen bygones, and the development of this market can, to a certain extent, be linked with the fashion for nostalgic farmhouse-style kitchens. Demand exists for kitchen accessories dating from Victorian times up to the kitsch gadgetry of the 1950s. Currently the more traditional looks are the most popular, though there is an increasing taste for Art Deco items, such as blue-and-white Cornish-ware. A set of late 19th-century cast-iron scales will cost between £50 and £100; antique plate racks sell for £75-150; and attractively carved Victorian bread boards for approximately £30.

The decorative quality of old kitchen accessories is usually the most important criterion. Most items will have reached the end of their functional lives — old electric irons and toasters are dangerous by modern standards, and copper pans with worn-out linings are unhygienic. Values do vary according to the amount of wear — chipped storage jars will always be less expensive than perfect ones.

Because the market is relatively young it is still possible to pick up items cheaply at jumble or car-boot sales. However, there are now some antique shops that deal exclusively in kitchenalia, and indications are that this is an area growing in popularity.

Right: A 'New Crown Jewel' mangle, by Jas. Mutch of Aberdeen, 63in (160cm) high. *£100.*

The 'Red Star' washing machine, by Beatty Bros. Limited, the circular washing tub with three iron hoops, the hinged cover with crank-handle and cast-iron spur-cog mechanism which turns the washing head with four pegs; horizontally mounted cast-iron mangle, embossed 'The Star Wringer', 49½in (125.5cm) high, *£60.*

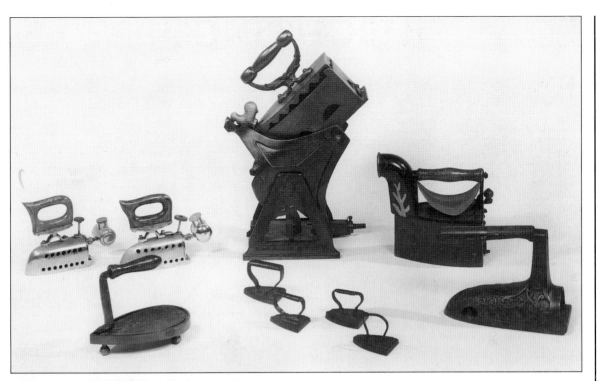

Above: A collection of 19th- and early 20th-century irons including two stainless-steel spirit irons, four small collar or lace irons, a German gas-fuelled iron with box, and a 'Kendrick' Carolina charcoal iron with painted funnel. *£15-60 each.*

Below: The 'New Shakespearian' butter churn; the wooden barrel, with four hinged and threaded lid clamps, revolves on twin rollers, upon a framed wooden base, detachable crank handle, 45½in (115cm) high. *£150.*

Above: The Napier patent coffee machine, *c.* 1845; the apparatus has a copper flask, condensing tube and beaker of up-turned bell form, glass spirit burner; the machine is suspended and housed within a gilt-metal frame on a ceramic base-plate edged with gilt, 13in (33cm). *£400.*

LIGHTING

Because many collectors will use their old lighting, it will almost inevitably have to be adapted to modern electrical requirements (although some purists insist on using old gas or oil lamps as they were originally intended). Collectable lighting need not necessarily be antique: 'Odeon' uplighters of the 1930s cost approximately £150 a pair and are much sought-after. As lighting is part of a home's decor, the collecting market is greatly influenced by shifts in taste — Art Nouveau 'Tiffany' one year, Art Deco the next — and prices will reflect that. The market for period lighting has given rise to a reproduction industry, and although copies of, say, Gallé lamps may be (and often are) well made, they have no collectable value.

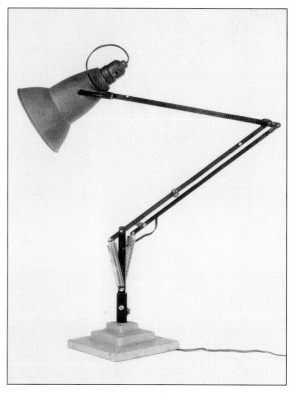

Above: A 1930s anglepoise lamp. *£30.*

Left, from left to right:
A Daum table lamp of etched and enamelled glass. The shade is etched 'Daum, Nancy' and the base is monogramed, 12in (31cm) high. *£7,200.* A Daum cameo glass table lamp. The shade is etched 'Daum, Nancy' and the base is monogramed, 18in (46cm) high. *£7,000.* A Gallé cameo glass table lamp. The base and shade have the Gallé cameo mark, 17¼in (44cm) high. *£8,500.*

MEDICAL COLLECTABLES

It is likely that the first items a collector will come across will be a miscellaneous assortment of nickel-plated and stainless-steel general practitioner's instruments: stethoscopes, glass syringes, sphygmomanometers (for taking blood pressure) and the like. At auction they will cost very little. Ophthalmic and dental instruments, although not found in profusion, can be acquired for reasonable prices. However, some dental equipment, such as a mid-18th-century tooth key with steel shaft and ebony handle, can sell for up to £200.

Eighteenth and 19th-century mahogany physicians' chests for carrying medicines and linaments sometimes have a secret compartment for poisons. These cabinets can fetch up to £1,000 if elaborate, but more standard versions may be bought for about £200. Mid-19th-century sets of ebony-handled surgical instruments in brass-bound mahogany cases can cost in excess of £1,000.

The best sources for identifying obscure old medical and surgical instruments are the original manufacturers' catalogues. Companies such as Allen and Hanbury or Downs produced comprehensive catalogues which are much sought-after by collectors.

A large Burke & Jones Culpeper-type microscope, 19th century. *£200.*

An Imperial Electric Supply Co machine, 1901, that administered a current of up to 200 volts of health-enhancing energy for only one penny. *£1,000.*

Below: A 1930s blood-pressure cuff and gauge. £20.

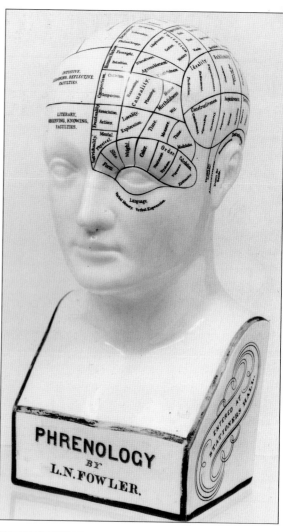

Below: A 19th-century mahogany apothecary's cabinet with labelled drawers, 86in (219cm) wide, 35in (89cm) high. £550.

Right: A 19th-century phrenology head, 11½in (28.75cm) high. £650.

MILITARIA & FIREARMS

The Special Air Services regiment memorial bears the inscription (a quote from James Elroy Flecker's 'Hassan'): 'We are the pilgrims, master; we shall go always a little further . . .' In terms of their dedication to research and acquisition, the SAS motto would be equally appropriate for that large band of militaria enthusiasts.

Many items of militaria (be it a medal awarded to a veteran of Waterloo, the uniform of a Victorian hussar, or the log-book of a Battle of Britain pilot) have a dramatic intimacy attached to them because they were often associated with life-and-death struggles. Awards for gallantry for example have, in most cases, the added advantage that their citations and the careers of their recipients can be researched.

Given the wide range of collectables in this area it is wise to concentrate on a theme. Some, for example, concentrate on a particular regiment or campaign; or they may collect medals bearing their own family surname.

Above: Lancer's cap (chapka), the large chapka-plate bearing battle honours and royal cypher of King Edward VII on red-velvet ground, and fitted with chin chain, complete with green regimental plume. £1,000.

Below: A rare flintlock 'Queen Anne'-style boxlock travelling pistol, *c.* 1770, Tower proof marks, brass frame engraved 'Grice, London', within scrollwork, replacement cock (*c.* 1810) with top jaw and screw missing, rounded Tutenag (Pak Tong) grip engraved with floral chains, the pommel deeply carved with a bird eating from an urn of flowers. £2,200.

Left, from left to right: 1st bn. The Royal Ulster Rifles; a regimental drum with blue cloth cover. £200–250. Regimental sidedrum of The Suffolk Regiment with cloth cover. £180–220. The Royal Regiment of Fusiliers' modern regimental drum. £180–220.

Above: One of 13 reproductions of Polish anti-German humorous cartoons, lampooning Hitler, Goering, Himmler and Co. *£100-150.*

Above: R. G. Ashby. 'Lieutenants Pritchard and Lloyd victorious in their Bristol fighter', watercolour, 11 x 17½in (28 x 45cm), overmounted and framed. *£150-200.*

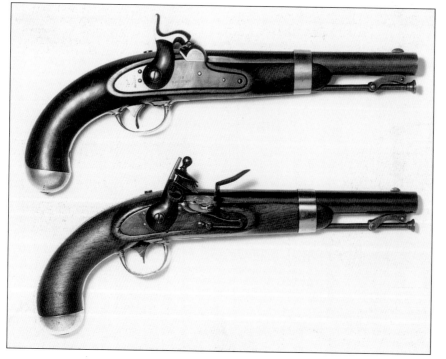

Left top: An American 28-bore military percussion holster pistol with initials 'U.S. J.P.C.' stamped at breech, the lock stamped 'U.S. H. Aston & Co., Middtn., Conn. 1851', half stocked with brass barrel-band and mounts. *£500.*

Left bottom: An American 28-bore military flintlock holster pistol, the lock stamped 'A. H. Waters & Co., Milbury, Mass.', surmounted by an eagle's head; brass pan, steel barrel-band and mounts. *£600.*

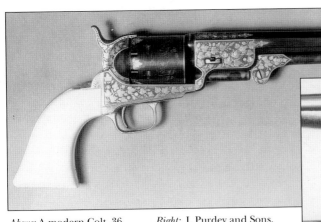

Above: A modern Colt .36 calibre model '1851 Navy' built *c.* 1970, hammer and frame profusely inlaid and overlaid in gold with fruiting vines by Ken Hunt, gold band around muzzle, 'Sam Colt' engraved on barrel, steel grip work and guard engraved with acanthus-leaf work and gold-plated, blued barrels and cylinder also inlaid with carved gold foliage, ivory grips, underside of barrel signed 'K.C.Hunt'. *£4,000.*

Right: J. Purdey and Sons. A trio of 12-bore, self-opening sidelock ejector guns, true cylinder, actions and locks engraved with rose and scrollwork retaining traces of colour, 14¼in (36.25cm) highly figured stocks. *£28,000.*

Left: A George Gibbs .375 H. & H. Mog double-barrelled boxlock ejector rifle, 26in (65cm) barrels, express sights, full scroll-engraved action, well figured 14in (35cm) stock with cheekpiece and rubber recoil pad. *£2,500.*

Below: A Mauser Luger, partridge foresight and adapted rear sight, replacement panel, chequered wooden grips. *£150.*

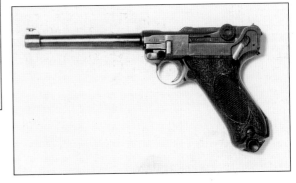

Above: A rare Thomas Bland and Son, Bland patent, self-cocking, 4-barrel pistol, .380 calibre, black powder only, retaining some original colour, chequered walnut bird's head grip/action plates, action at fault, engraved on the grip 'The Monostriker Pistol'. *£400.*

Above: A German close helmet (reputed to be the funerary helmet of Justin of Nassau), late 16th century, height 16in (41cm). £800–1,200.

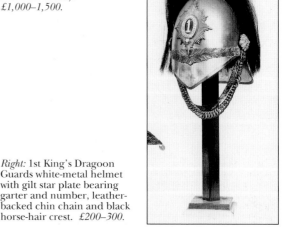

Above: 12th Lancers, Victorian officer's chapka, large brass regimental plate bearing battle honours for Peninsula, Waterloo and Sevastopol, V.R. cypher on plume boss (lacks plume and chin chain). £1,000–1,500.

Right: 2nd County of London Imperial Yeomanry white-metal helmet with gilt star plate, leather-backed chin chain and red horse-hair crest. £200–300.

Right: 1st King's Dragoon Guards white-metal helmet with gilt star plate bearing garter and number, leather-backed chin chain and black horse-hair crest. £200–300.

Left: A complete suit of armour in the style of the 16th century, comprising close helmet with bevor and two-piece visor pierced with ventilation slits; gorget, arm defences comprising pauldrons, upper and lower defences, elbow couters and long-cuffed gauntlets, articulated fingers, cuirass with tassets of four simulated lames, full leg defences with articulated sabatons with shields and glaive-guisarme, all etched with floral sprays and trophies of arms, mounted on stand. *£600–800.*

Above: The dress uniform of an officer of the Queen's Own Dorset Yeomanry, consisting of full-dress tunic with scarlet facings, second lieutenant's rank star on collar, pouch belt with silver accoutrements, mess jacket and waistcoat and overalls with silver lace stripes. *£300–500.*

Right: A set of four cast Grenadier Guards, the well-modelled soldiers shown kneeling and standing on wooden plinths with applied presentation plaques. *£4,200.*

Right: Major C. R. Spedding, DSO, Royal Irish Rifles. A group of six medals including DSO, Queen's South Africa Medal (with three clasps), King's South Africa Medal (with two clasps), 1914 Star (with 5 Aug - 22 Nov 1914 bar), British War Medal 1914-18 and Victory Medal. *£420.*

Below: A pre-World War II German officer's sword, with brassed-metal handle and guard, Anton Wingen blade, and metal scabbard, blade 32¼in (82cm). *£300-500.*

A World War II German naval officer's dagger, brass trim and scabbard, silver-braid furniture, dagger 14½in (37cm). *£80-120.*

A World War II German naval officer's dagger, with E. & F. Horster-engraved blade, brass trim and scabbard, dagger 14½in (38cm). *£60-80.*

A late World War II German naval dagger, with brassed die-cast trim, E. & F. Horster-engraved blade, and scabbard, dagger 15in (38cm). *£50-80.*

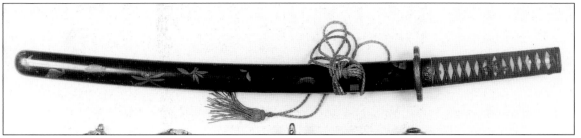

Below, left to right:
A Royal Navy officer's sword, the etched blade by Henry Wilkinson with royal arms, fouled anchor, oak leaves, etc., the gilt-metal solid guard with rear quillon and folding side guard, copper wire-bound grip, lion's head pommel, in its gilt-mounted leather scabbard, blade 31in (79cm). £150-200.

A Persian shamshir, plain, curved, single-edged blade, white-metal crosspiece, ivory grips, in its leather scabbard with white-metal mounts, blade 30in (76cm). £150-200.

An early 18th-century Indian sword tulwar, broad curved single-edged damascus-steel blade with long clipped back tip, struck with double crescent armourer's mark, all gold damascened with foliate sprays, in its green velvet-covered wooden scabbard. £150-200.

A United States model 1860 light cavalry sabre, the single-edged curved blade back-edged towards the points, stamped at the forte 'Chicopee Mass. & U.S. M.M. 1864', the two-bar guard of brass, the grip leather bound, the metal scabbard with two loose rings, blade 34⅛in (88cm). £100-150.

An Elizabeth II Royal Air Force officer's sword, the blade by Wilkinson etched with royal arms, RAF eagle, blank scrolls, etc., gilt-brass guard with eagle and monogram, eagle's head pommel, wire-bound white fishskin covered grip, the black patent-leather scabbard with brass mounts, with leather scabbard cover, blade 32in (82cm). £350-450.

Above: A Japanese Wakizachi, contained in its lacquered saya decorated with grasshoppers and dragonflies complete with koduzka decorated with mice, blade 17⅜in (45cm). £120-180.

Left: A Russian teardrop-shaped green glass scent bottle, with gilt-metal mounts and suspensory chains, the glass overpainted with a cannon, an inscription, and dated 1876. £150-200.

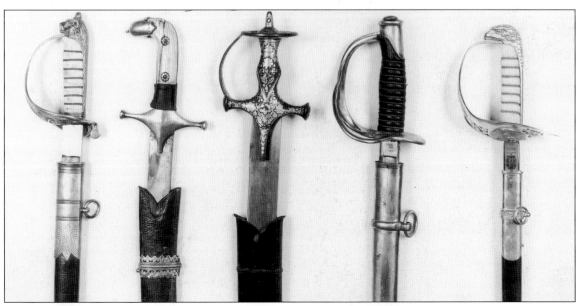

MODEL SHIPS

The most prestigious and expensive ship models (a fine example can cost £100,000!) were those made for the Admiralty Board in the 17th and 18th centuries. The first, of the 'Prince Royal', was built in 1607 by Phineas Pett. During the Napoleonic wars many French prisoners in England were sailors and craftsmen in ivory, and were able to make accurate and delicate model ships in bone; they also worked in boxwood. The bone models are highly prized; a fine specimen can cost £10,000, while a boxwood version will cost half that.

Half-block models were made by 19th-century shipwrights to serve as three-dimensional plans. The most collectable have laminated ('bread and butter') wood hulls. Prices at auction range from £150 to £1,000. 'Sailors' models', made by fishermen and sailors, mainly in the 19th century, should combine accuracy with a certain robust naïveté. They will cost £200-800. There is also a whole range of pond yachts and radio-controlled boats which can be found for well under £1,000.

Above: An exhibition-standard static model of the 'Royal Caroline', by Mario Paolini, the planked hull with similar decks, finely detailed with ship's launch, throne, lanterns, tiller, rope coils, hinged doors, glazed windows, gratings, capstan, pumps, stairways, carved figurehead, anchors, showing 16 guns, flying pennant and flags, the three masts with full standing and running rigging, her sails unfurled, 33½in (85cm) overall length. *£4,000–6,000.*

Above: A static model of the Dutch second-rater 'Friesland', by Len Hooley, 1979, the plank on a frame hull with similar decks, modelled showing 74 of her 78 guns, her decks detailed with gratings, balustrades, two ship's boats, rope coils, capstan, anchors and figurehead, her three masts and bowsprit with full standing and running rigging, flying pennants and flags, 31in (79cm) overall length. *£8,500.*

Left: A wooden model of the paddle steamer 'King of the Mississippi', the single-paddle vessel with deck details, including bridge, ship's wheel, ship's bell, twin funnels, companionways and hand rails, hoists with gangplanks and capstan, mounted in a glazed mahogany case, 31¼in (79.5cm) wide. *£600–800.*

Right: A static display model of the French man-o'-war 'Royal Louis', modelled as at 1780, the planked wood hull with three masts, standing and running rigging, full complement of sails, stern with twin galleries, the beakhead with figurehead, and deck details including brass cannon, 42½in (107.5cm) long. £2,000–3,000.

Below: A static display model of the clipper ship 'Thermopylae' built by David Bradley of Patcham, 35½in (90cm) long. £520.

Below: A static model of the mid-19th-century French steam paddle and sail troopship 'L'Orenoque', built by Len Hooley, the plank on frame hull with similar decks, detailed with three ship's boats on davits, two others lashed down, cannons, railings, stairways, wheel, a single funnel, ventilators, hatches, rope coils and a capstan, her three masts with full standing and running rigging, 34½in (87.5cm) overall length. £550.

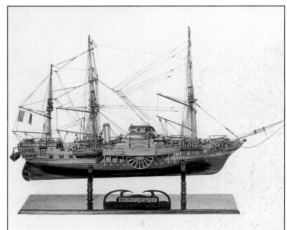

Below: A fibreglass pond model of the steam torpedo boat S.306, with searchlight, smoke stack, torpedo tubes, twin machine-gun turrets, Bofors fore and aft, navigation lights and railings, fitted with electric motor, 48½in (123cm) long. £140.

Left: A fibreglass, wood and metal ¼:1in scale model of the deepsea trawler 'Milford Star', built by Néul Howard Pritchard of Blackpool; deck details include windlass, trawl winch, cleats, hand rails, stone pipes, trawl gallows and gratings, deckhouse and bridge with ship's wheel, binnacle and telegraph, fitted with Beuler 6V motor, single screw, and radio control, transmitter and stand, 36¼in (89cm) long. £400–600.

MODERN FURNITURE

This relatively new area for collectors really starts with furniture designed or influenced by the German Bauhaus movement of the 1920s which was preoccupied with the idea that form should follow function. The advent of new materials such as chrome-plated tubular steel allowed designers to expose what had hitherto been hidden (the frame) and make it paramount. Such tubular furniture became fashionable during the 1930s and the designs of leading practitioners such as Breuer percolated through to mass-manufacturers (an original Breuer chair can fetch over £25,000 at auction).

Post-1945 designers took advantage of laminated and heat-moulded woods as well as hard and soft plastics in strong colours. Italy (Fornasetti, Bellini, Columbo) led the way, with important designers coming from France (Paulin), the USA (Eames, Saarinen) and Scandinavia (Arne Jacobsen). In Britain, designers tended to be more conservative, but recently designers such as John Makepeace and Alan Peters who, while echoing some of the ideas of the Arts and Crafts movement, are making pieces in the forefront of international modern furniture design.

Left: 'Rimorchiatore', a lamp by Gae Aulenti (Italy), formed as a tugboat, designed for Candle, c. 1969, with hooded lamp, vase and container, white painted metal, 14½in (37cm) high. £220.

Below: A floor lamp by Jean-Pierre Vitrac (France) for Verre Lumière, 1970, the sphere opening to reveal six segments, each with internal light. £1,250.

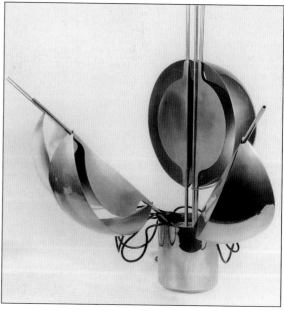

Above: An Astre lamp by Yonel Lebovici (France), c. 1972, the revolving tiltable disc with four peripheral globes, two with directional halogen lights, on a triangular base, stainless steel, engraved 'Lebovici Y, EA', 26in (66cm) high. £1,100.

Near right: A birch-wood sideboard by Robert Heritage (UK), for G. W. Evans, 1954, the black lacquered rectangular top above three drawers, and a pair of cupboard doors flanking a flap drawer, decorated with a city scene, on four pierced-metal legs 54in (137cm) wide, 17in (43cm) deep. £1,800.

Far right: 'Harpchair', an easy chair by Jorgen Hovelskov, *c.* 1957, the wooden frame restrung, 55½in (128cm) high. £260.

Left: A rectangular coffee table by Piero Fornasetti (Italy), the top printed with four rectangular panels depicting still lives, on gilt-metal crossed legs, 17⅛in (45cm) high, 42½in (108cm) wide, 24in (61cm) deep. £750.

Below, left: A semi-spherical fauteuil by Christian Daninos (France), 1968, moulded perspex on circular iron base, 47¼in (120cm) high. £800.

Below, right: A clear acrylic easy chair by Ross Molinary (Italy), for Totam, 1968, 26¾in (68cm) high. £350.

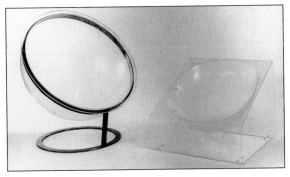

Above, left: A moulded figural chair by Ruth Francken (France), designed 1971, black fibre-glass with square loop metal base, stamped '1986, R.F.21/300', 39⅓in (100cm) high. £2,000.

Above, right: 'Ron Ron' Ultrafurniture by Marion Baruch, designed for Simon, *c.* 1969, black tufted spherical form with matching tail, 31⅛in (80cm) diam. £400.

Near right: An easy chair, *c.* 1965, scrolled aluminium base, covered with foam and striped PVC-coated cloth, 30in (76½cm) high. £400.

Far right: A wire armchair attributed to Joseph A. Motte (France), *c.* 1962, of parallel chrome-steel rods forming a cube with inset brown-covered latex cushion, 26¾in (68cm) high, 29in (73½cm) wide. £700.

MUSICAL INSTRUMENTS

Each area of this very diverse field, be it woodwind, brass, keyboard, or plucked and bowed instruments, has its devotees. Nor should we forget the electric guitar — a classic 1960s Gibson can fetch several thousand pounds. Due to this diversity, collectors have to research their particular field of interest. For example, with violins there are many copies of Stradivarius, Amati and Guarneri which can easily mislead the unwary. With early acoustic guitars it is a little easier. The makers of the early to mid-19th century decorated them with a heavy inlay of mother-of-pearl, usually in the form of floral borders around the sound hole and along the neck. For some collectors, the more elaborate the inlay the more desirable the instrument (guitars by René Lucotte of Paris or Louis Panormo of London, for example, fetch up to £2,000, depending on condition).

Early woodwind instruments are also sought-after, particularly if German, French or English. The maker's name is often branded on each joint, and a specimen by a great maker (for example, an 18th-century flute by Thomas Stanesbury Junior) can fetch as much as £18,000.

Below: An early Victorian rosewood duet stand, the easel music rests with foliate scroll fretwork panels, on a plain turned column and outswept tripod support, 67in (170cm) high. *£6,000.*

Above, left: An American violin by Knute Reindahl, labelled 'Knute Reindahl 10=27 Chicago 1904, No. 253', the one-piece back of handsomely marked maple of broad to medium curl, the ribs of similar curl, the scroll of a plainer wood, the table of fine to medium grain, the varnish of a golden-brown colour, length of back 14⅛in (36.2cm), with case and cover. *£1,000–1,500.*

Above, right: A French violin, *c.* 1850, the one-piece back of medium to narrow horizontal curl, the ribs and scroll of a similar curl, the table of medium and even grain, the varnish of a golden-red colour, length of back 14⅛in (35.8cm). *£3,000–4,000.*

Above: A miniature violin, with sycamore body and ebony fret board, with accompanying fiddle, in a fitted leather case, 7in (18cm) long with case. *£120–180.*

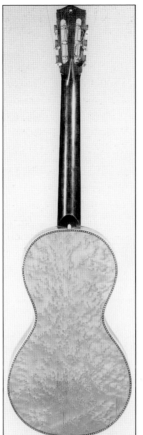

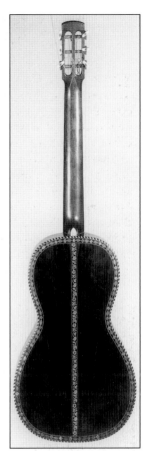

Above: Front and back of a French guitar by Pettit Jean, Mirecourt, *c.* 1810, branded by the maker internally, the one-piece back veneered with handsomely figured bird's-eye maple, the edges inlaid with mother-of-pearl and ebony forming a repeating chevron pattern, the outer edge an ivory band, the ribs of solid bird's-eye maple, the table of broad to fine grain opening towards the flanks, the edging inlaid with mother-of-pearl and mastic to form a repeating floral pattern that continues into the neck, the sound hole with similar design, the ebony neck set with nickel frets, the upper-note frets set into the table, the ebony head with brass machine heads and ivory buttons. *£1,500–2,000.*

Above: Front and back of a fine Italian guitar, *c.* 1890, the two-piece back of rosewood veneer, the edging inlaid with mother-of-pearl and mastic forming a floral design enclosed by fruitwood borders, the outer edging of ebony and ivory lozenges, the centre joint decorated with fruitwood inlay set with abalone shell also forming a floral design, the ribs of rosewood veneer with fruitwood inlay, the table of medium grain, the sound hole set with semi-circles of mother-of-pearl intricately engraved to show floral scenes, all enclosed by fruitwood banding, length of back 17½in (44.5cm), with case. *£1,500–2,000.*

Left: A Regency rosewood grained and parcel-gilt harp, the fluted upright decorated with classical motifs and anthemion, the base with winged seahorses, on gilded paw feet, the brass fretboard stamped 'Patent Harp invented by T. A. Stumpff of London'. *£8,500.*

Above: Square piano by John Broadwood & Sons, No. 33277, *c.* 1825, in original condition, 5½ octaves. Case: mahogany with rosewood cross-banding and beaded moulding, white label name board with pierced brass frets, supported on six turned and lobed legs. *£1,000.*

Right: Ascherberg grand No. 2590, 1880, overstrung with Ascherberg patented action, 85-note compass with original ivory keyboard. Case: rosewood, profusely inlaid with urns, ribbons and floral scrolls, on turned tapered legs with boxwood stringing. *£2,000.*

Grand piano by John Brinsmead No. 57125, *c.* 1905, 88-note compass with original ivory keyboard and tied action. Case: rosewood with scrolled floral inlay supported on turned tapered legs. *£2,500.*

Broadwood upright No. 59440, 1884, straight-strung underdamper with metal screw plank, 85-note compass with good ivory keyboard and unichorder. Case: satinwood and mahogany with inlay depicting floral swags, bouquets and musical instruments, the keyboard supported on similarly decorated columns, with scrolled candelabra. *£1,500.*

NAUTICALIA

Nauticalia embraces a diverse area of collectables including paintings, commemorative objects, seafaring craftwork (see, for example, Scrimshaw, page 141) and pottery (one of the most popular Staffordshire Toby jugs of the 19th century was 'Rodney's Sailor' — a jolly tar seated with a glass in his hand and a handy jug by his side).

Navigational instruments are widely collected, and the most common is the sextant. A good example, made of brass and contained in a wooden-box, will cost about £300. If it has a lattice-work frame with a central bell-shaped panel, it will be nearer £450. The forerunner of the sextant — the octant — was normally made of ebony and will sell for £200-500.

Printed ephemera associated with the great pre-1939 shipping lines (brochures, menu-cards, posters and sailing lists etc.) are still plentiful and not expensive.

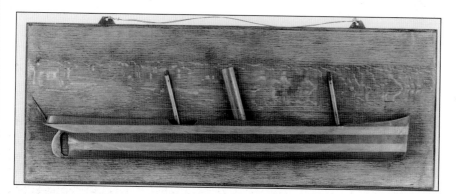

Left: A shipbuilder's half-block model of a steam sailing yacht, the laminated wood hull with truncated raked masts and funnel, mounted on an oak backboard, 37in (93cm) wide. *£200.*

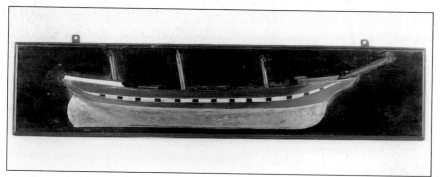

Left: A half-block model of a clipper ship, the painted hull with rudder, bowsprit and three truncated raked masts, mounted on a mahogany backboard, 32in (82cm) wide. *£180-250.*

Left: A Dixon & Co. pink-lustre pottery circular plate, well-printed in black with the inscription, 'Mate Sound the Pump Morning, Noon and Night', within a floral cartouche, the rim splashed with a pink-lustre glaze, 8½in (21.5cm) diam. *£130.*

Right: A rectangular pink-lustre-ware pottery plate, the moulded scalloped edge splashed with pink lustre, enclosing a clipper ship, printed in black and enamelled in green, ochre and yellow, 9½in (24cm) wide. *£600.*

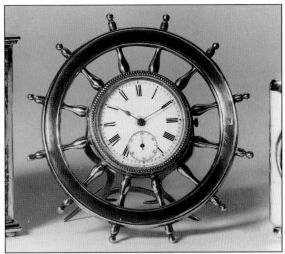

Above: A silver timepiece of ship's-wheel form, the watch movement set within the spokes with strut support, 4in (10cm) diam., Mappin & Webb, Sheffield, 1908. *£190.*

Left: Sir Leslie Ward, 'Spy' (English, 1851-1922) Caricature of the Duke of Leeds. Originally for 'Vanity Fair'. Watercolour and gouache, signed, unframed. 21 x 14⅝in (53.3 x 36.8cm). *£200-400.*

Above: A shellwork sailor's valentine, Barbadian, *c.* 1900, the hinged twin octagonal mahogany case with coloured shell collages and the lettering 'A present from Barbados 1901', 18¾in (47.5cm) wide. *£300.*

Left: A shipping diorama, English, 19th century, the shaped and painted waterline half-model of a schooner with rigging and painted wood sails, mounted on a simulated sea, in a glazed case with a painted seascape background, 30¾in (78cm) wide. *£360.*

Left: A George IV silver yachting trophy cup, 8½in (21.8cm) high, the sides chased with flowers, scrolls and racing yachts, engraved inscription to side 'Royal Yorkshire Yacht Club Presented by John Loft, Esq. Sheriff', London 1825, by John Bridge. £700-900.

Below: A Japanese 'Mermaid', late 18th/early 19th century, the dried head, ribcage and front claws made from a monkey's body, attached to a fish tail with dorsal and tail fins, mounted in a rectangular glass case, 14½in (37cm) long. These creatures were supposedly caught at sea, but were actually elaborate hoaxes originating from S.E. Asia, especially Japan. £1,320.

Below: A decorative gilt-metal neff, with plank on frame hull, detailed stern gallery and bows, the three masts with a suit of sails upon a stylised sea base, heightened with enamelled armorial shield and pennants, 24in (60cm) overall length, 26½in (66.25cm) high. £2,000-3,000.

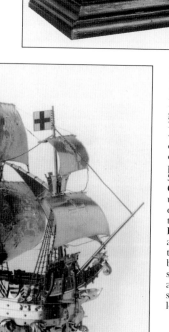

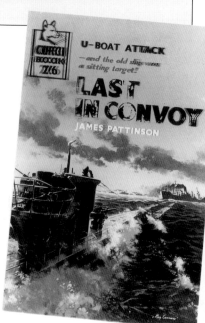

Right: Roy Carnon. 'Last in Convoy', by James Pattinson, gouache, signed. 27 x 18in (68.7 x 45.7cm) with original acetate overlay and hand-painted titles. The S.S. 'Regal Gesture' brought up the rear of a convoy of 45 ships travelling from Halifax to England and due to engine trouble was left behind. Enemy submarines attacked her and she suffered high losses. £200-300.

PENS

The history of the fountain pen, at least from the point of view of the collector, began in 1884, when Lewis Edson Waterman patented an 'improved reservoir pen' in the USA, with George S. Parker and Mabie-Todd and Bond following suit within the decade. Other penmakers, notably Mont Blanc in Germany and De La Rue in the UK, who also had connections in the stationery trade, grew into profitable international companies alongside the Americans. Pens from these companies are of worldwide interest to collectors today, while those from other manufacturers tend to have a smaller following in their own countries: Conway Stewart (UK), Pelikan and Kaweko (Germany), Eclipse (Canada), Wahl-Eversharp, and Conklin (USA).

The collecting enthusiasm for fountain pens began in the USA in the early 1980s and pen conventions are now regularly attended by affluent professionals. Interest in the UK burgeoned towards the end of the 1980s and has tended to concentrate on a broader spectrum, not just on the expensive end of the market.

Many collectors follow one 'marque' but often specialise within it, for instance in 'eye-dropper' pens (1884-1915), safety retractable pens (1908-25) or Art Deco plastic pens (1921-30). Since the late 1980s the price of solid-gold pens and those overlaid with precious-metal filigree has leapt up, with 'oversized' pens commanding top prices.

Some typical prices are: 14ct solid-gold Waterman *c.* 1905, £3,000; silver filigree *c.* 1915, £1,000; Art Deco Waterman Patrician, £400; 1920s Parker Big Red, £100. However, thousands of good-quality and still-useable pens from the 1880s onwards can be bought at flea markets or auctions from £10.

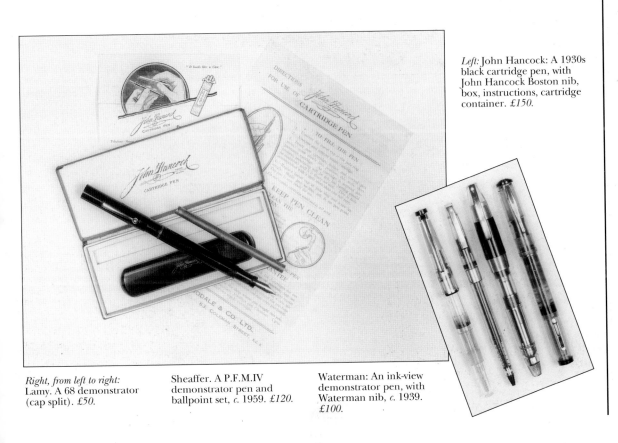

Left: John Hancock: A 1930s black cartridge pen, with John Hancock Boston nib, box, instructions, cartridge container. *£150.*

Right, from left to right: Lamy. A 68 demonstrator (cap split). *£50.*

Sheaffer. A P.F.M.IV demonstrator pen and ballpoint set, *c.* 1959. *£120.*

Waterman: An ink-view demonstrator pen, with Waterman nib, *c.* 1939. *£100.*

Left, from top:
A green/brown/black marble Swan Visofil, with decorative pierced cap-band, c. 1936. £50.

A green marble Swan Leverless L470-66, with broad 18ct gold cap-band, c. 1939. £80.

A jade Swan Self-Filler No. 142-50 and matching Fyne-Poynt pencil, c. 1930. £150.

A cream-veined brown-marble Swan Leverless EZ pen, with one milled and two plain gold-plated cap-bands, c. 1935. £50.

An unusual lady's Swan self-filler pen, in dove grey with one broad pink and two narrow green/black edged bands at the top and base of the cap, c. 1930. £50.

A cracked-ice Conway-Stewart 58 Duro pen, still retaining original price band, c. 1950. £120.

A maroon/black lined Conway-Stewart 58 Duro pen, still retaining original price band, c. 1950. £50.

A red/black lined Conway-Stewart 73, still retaining original price band, c. 1950. £50.

A green/bronze Wahl-Eversharp gold seal pen with single decorative cap-band, c. 1929. £150.

A jade-green Sheaffer Lifetime Senior 'Flat Top', fitted with Sheaffer nib, c. 1928. £80.

Far left:
An Onoto Magna, fitted with a No. 7 Co-Respondent nib, c. 1936. £80.

Right, from top:
A red Parker Lucky Curve Duofold Senior, with twin cap-bands and 'arrow' nib, *c.* 1929. £100.

A black/pearl Waterman Patrician pen, with nickel trim and large Patrician nib, *c.* 1929. £200.

A turquoise Waterman Patrician pen, fitted with Patrician nib, *c.* 1929. £300.

A chased black hard rubber Weidlich eye-dropper pen, with two chased gold-plated bands, *c.* 1915. £40.

A chased black rubber Sheaffer 3.5, lever-filled, with broad gold-plated cap-band, *c.* 1915. £120.

A limited-editon Parker '105' Royal Wedding pen, issued to commemorate the wedding of HRH the Prince of Wales to the Lady Diana Spencer, No. 111 of 1,000. £200.

A jade Parker Lucky Curve Lady Duofold, with three cap-bands and ribbon ring, *c.* 1928. £50.

A black Parker Lucky Curve Duofold Special, with twin cap-bands, *c.* 1928. £90.

A red Parker Lucky Curve Senior Duofold, with twin cap-bands, *c.* 1928. £100.

Far right:
A Waterman Patrician desk pen, fitted with Waterman yellow nib, *c.* 1928. £60.

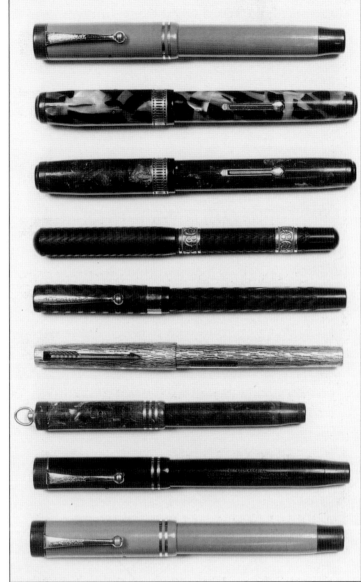

Left: The Waterman 'Pen Prophet' 1922-30 in contemporary blue bindings with gilt tooling, three volumes containing Spring, Summer and Christmas numbers for nine years (28 numbers in all, as 1927 has an extra Autumn number.) Each number has colour front and back covers, many have colour illustrations inside, and the later issues have fold-out colour centre pages. The contents include details of models from the golden years of the 1920s, from safety pens up to the Patrician line. As well as many unusual and presentation pens we read of the factories in England and the United States, visits abroad and gatherings of the executives of the Waterman company and progress of the Waterman family. The 'Pen Prophet' contains many period advertising campaigns for Waterman pens and pencils, as well as hints to salesmen and testimonials from celebrities frequently photographed with their favourite Waterman model. £2,000-3,000.

Left, from top:
A red/black mottled De La Rue 7273-90 lever-filler pen, with Onoto nib, *c.* 1934. £50.

A multicoloured 'Tiny Dot' miniature pen, with warranted nib, *c.* 1920. £40.

An unusual red/black mottled Wyvern baby eye-dropper pen, with warranted nib, *c.* 1920. £40.

A red Parker Lucky Curve Senior pen with twin cap-bands, *c.* 1927. £150.

A red Conway-Stewart 759 pen, *c.* 1920. £50.

A De La Rue 5501-37 with transparent barrel, *c.* 1937. £50.

A lapis-blue Parker Junior Duofold pencil, *c.* 1927. £100.

A red Parker Streamline Duofold Special, with twin cap-bands, *c.* 1929. £50.

A Parker Shadow-Wave Vacumatic pencil, *c.* 1939. £40.

A black Mont Blanc 134 Masterpiece pen, with oblique tin nib, *c.* 1940. £120.

Far left:
A silver overlaid eye-dropper pen, with black hard rubber over/underfeed nib, London, 1911. £120.

Right:
A fine Namiki pen and pencil set decorated in lacquer inlaid with paui shell, depicting pheasants beside a flowing stream; together with Namiki presentation box and instructions for use, *c.* 1930. £3,000.

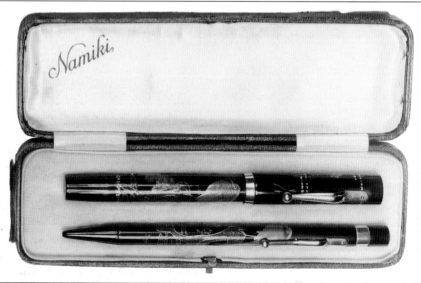

Right, from top:
A red-ripple Waterman 51V, fitted with No. 1 Ideal nib, *c.* 1925. *£50.*

A Dunhill-Namiki lacquer pen, decorated with paui shells inlaid as flowers, *c.* 1930. *£120.*

A Namiki lacquer lady's pen, decorated with inlaid paui shell circles and 14ct gold cap-band, *c.* 1930. *£300.*

A black Mont Blanc 1M safety pen, fitted with No. 1 Simple nib. *£100.*

A black hard rubber Mont Blanc safety pen with white-star cap and florally chased gold-plated bands, *c.* 1923. *£60.*

A red-ripple Waterman 55V pen, with ring on cap, *c.* 1926. *£60.*

A brown-lizard Waterman 92 pen, with three decorative gold-plated bands, *c.* 1933. *£80.*

A shiny black chased hard rubber Waterman No. 16 pen, with two decorative gold-plated bands, *c.* 1915. *£200.*

Far right:
An Onoto Magna, fitted with No. 7 nib, *c.* 1938. *£50.*

Outside right:
A black chased hard rubber Waterman 58, with nickel lever and No. 8 nib, *c.* 1923. *£50.*

Right, left to right:
A Parker '51' Insignia, with burgundy section, *c.* 1960. *£70.*

A rare Parker '85' pen and ballpoint set in vermeille (gold plate on silver) with bark finish, *c.* 1975. *£130.*

A fine 18ct gold Parker 'Flamme 65' pen, pencil and ballpoint set, *c.* 1968. *£1,000.*

A 9ct gold Presidential '61' pen and pencil set, decorated with engine-turning in the fine barley pattern, *c.* 1972. *£210.*

A 14ct gold '51' with plain body and cap, *c.* 1949. *£520.*

Bottom: A '51' Vacumatic with tan body and gold-plated cap, and applied with pearl studs at each end of the pen, *c.* 1945. *£85.*

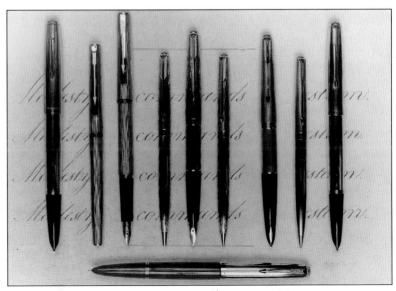

PERFUME BOTTLES

Although perfume manufacturing has changed little since the turn-of-the-century, the containers have evolved from pharmaceutical jars to stylish works of art. For each new perfume a wide range of containers was needed to present the product, and the bottle became the symbol that reflected the quality and characteristics of the contents. Imaginative bottles became ever more important for the perfume trade and it was quite common for the most respected artists and decorators of the day to design chic flacons, the cost of which may have been greater than the perfume they held.

The period between 1900 and 1940 is regarded as being the 'golden age' of the perfume bottle. The 1920s and 30s witnessed a period of unprecedented growth in the industry, and the mechanisation of mould-blown glass, and the employment of top designers such as Lalique and Baccarat, transformed commercial scent bottles into exciting presentation pieces, designed to evoke a mood and tempt the eye.

Above, from left to right:
An opaque black glass scent bottle for Volnay of circular flask form, moulded with an allover design of overlapping flowerheads and with matching disc stopper, 5⅛ in (13cm), base moulded Volnay, Paris. *£700.*

An oval bottle for Christian Dior, with black and white 'tweed' label and matching plastic stopper, in oval 'tweed', zipped case with 'Miss Dior' label, 4⅓in (11cm). *£100.*

'Flèches', a smoky grey frosted bottle for Lancôme, of oval section, flaring at the top, with a gilt metal vertical band on the front, the arrow-shaped stopper with gilt metal cap, applied white metal label, 6⅛in (15cm). *£440.*

Above, top:
'Adoration' a gilt-encased bottle moulded as a sealed Indo-Chinese god, his gilt metal head forming the stopper, 7¼in (18.5cm). *£360.*

Above, left to right:
'Subtitle' for Houbigant, a Baccarat clear glass bottle, moulded as a figure of a seated Buddha, the spherical stopper with gilt ring handle, gilt label, 3¼in (8.5cm), in black shrine-shaped case with front opening panels. *£580.*

'Chu Chin Chow', an enamelled blue bottle for Bryenne, moulded as a seated fat Chinese dignitary, enamelled detail in pink and green, embellished with gilt, his head and collar covering the stopper, 2½in (6.5cm), signed 'G. K. Benda', (cover chipped). *£450.*

'Ming Toy', a Baccarat bottle for Forest, moulded as a seated geisha, enamelled detail of blue, black and gilt, with gilt fan-shaped stopper, 4¼in (11cm), (crack to stopper base). *£1,800.*

Right, top:
A gilt enamelled ruby glass perfume flask of faceted conical form enamelled with scrolls and foliage, gilt metal scroll mount and hinged cover, the whole resembling a dagger, on gilt suspension chain, 5⅛in (13cm). *£200.*

Right, from left to right:
A clear glass perfume pendant of bulbous teardrop form enclosed in an ornate scrolling white metal and gilt mount and with filigree metal 'crown' stopper, on suspension chain, 2⅜in (7cm). *£120.*

A clear glass and gilt overlay perfume flask, of flattened teardrop form, overlaid with filigree decoration and with ribbed gilt stopper, 4¼in (11cm), in silk-lined leathered case. *£200.*

A cobalt blue and white overlay perfume flask, of slender tapering form, with chased gilt metal cover, 4¼in (11cm). *£100.*

A clear glass double travelling perfume flask, cut with a lozenge design, with chased gilt metal mounts and covers, 5in (12.8cm). *£100.*

A clear glass double travelling perfume flask cut with a zig-zag design, with gilt metal mounts and chased screw tops, 4¾in (12cm). *£95.*

A ruby and clear glass double travelling perfume flask, the glass with a lozenge design, each end with chased white metal mount and cover, 5½in (14cm). *£150.*

A clear glass double travelling perfume flask, with lozenge and diamond decoration, each end with silver gilt mounts and covers, 6½in (16cm), stamped London hallmarks for 1874. *£140.*

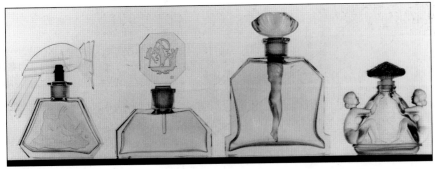

Above, from left to right:
A Baccarat shaped triangular bottle, intaglio moulded with a figure teasing a woodpecker, the stopper moulded as a large woodpecker, 6⅜in (16cm). *£280.*

Part of a set of three clear and blue shaded bottles, of curved triangular form with white metal collars and diamond cut-glass stoppers, encased in a pierced cylindrical white metal mount, 4¾in (12cm). *£200.*

'Ramses', a crystal bottle for Ramses Inc., of stepped rectangular section with chamfered shoulders, the ribbed lotus flower stopper suspending a nude female figure dipper, 7⅝in (19.5cm). *£250.*

A frosted and clear glass bottle, of rounded triangular form, flanked by two female nude figures, seated at the base of the bottle, with shallow conical moulded foliate stopper, heightened with green and amethyst staining, 5in (12.7cm). *£210.*

Above: 'Hantise', a Baccarat black enamelled pink opaque bottle for A. Gravier, gilt metal bullet-shaped stopper and circular foot, the body enamelled with a scales design and flower sprays, 4⅝ in (11.7cm). Below it, a 'Hantise' face powder box, 3½in (9cm). *£2,500 the pair.*

Above, from left to right:
A clear and blue stained scent bottle for Forvil, cylindrical, moulded overall with flowerheads between branches, with matching flat circular stopper, 4⅝in (11.8cm), moulded R. Lalique, Paris, France. £320.

'Sans Adieu', a clear green scent bottle for Worth, flattened circular with 'Worth' moulded in the bottle, and stepped disc stopper, 3in (7.5cm),

moulded R. Lalique France, numbered. £450.

'Sans Adieu', a clear green scent bottle for Worth, cylindrical with stepped disc stopper, on original square metal wood base, impressed 'WORTH ', bottle 4¼in (10.8cm), moulded R. Lalique. £450.

'Morabito No. 7', an amber opalescent bottle for Morabito, of compressed ovoid form, with flat circular rim, on oval base, moulded with

four turtles, the spherical stopper with turtle shell markings, 5½in (14cm), base moulded in intaglio 'Morabito No. 7 Paris', etched Lalique France. £4,600.

'Vers le Jour', an amber frosted and clear scent bottle for Worth, flat circular, moulded with a repeating triangular design with matching stopper, 5⅛in (13cm), moulded R. Lalique, France. £2,000.

'Méplat Deux Figurines', a clear and frosted scent bottle, the rectangular bottle enclosing a plaque moulded in intaglio with two nude female figures amongst flowering branches, the stopper moulded as two nude female figures holding up a garland of flowers, 5¼in (13.5cm), engraved R. Lalique, France. £7,200.

Above, outside pair: A pair of Paris scent bottles with globular stoppers, each of square-cut cornered form, with elongated neck, enamelled with floral sprays, interspaced by gilt enrichments, all on an apricot ground, 7in (18cm) high, *c.* 1855. £310.

Above, centre: Two Paris porcelain perfume bottles with stoppers, each of hexagonal- sided form, each with figural decoration on alternating black and white ground, interspaced by blue and gilt decoration, 19th century. £140 each.

Above: 'Voltigy', a Baccarat clear bottle for A. Gravier, modelled as a butterfly with outstretched wings, the body stained in pink and black, moulded with Voltigy A. Gravier, 5⅜in (9.2cm), with paper label and sealed, in fitted leatherette box. £3,000.

PHOTOGRAPHIC EQUIPMENT

The enthusiasm for collecting cameras and photographic images is growing in popularity. Photography is an acknowledged art form and cameras are widely appreciated as innovative and often attractive bygones. At the turn of the century, photography was generally the domain of the wealthy. The brass-bound mahogany plate cameras and the photographic materials they required were expensive, while early photographers often needed servants to carry and prepare the equipment.

Early mahogany cameras, especially those by Sanderson, Thornton Pickard and Houghton, were beautifully made with leather bellows, brass fittings and ingenious wooden tripods. Similarly, the pictures taken during this period often turn up for sale in expensively-bound photographic albums that reveal images of life in a world we can hardly recognise today.

By the onset of World War I, the advent of mass-produced and inexpensive cameras and the availability of the roll film, pioneered by George Eastman's Kodak Company, led to the popularisation of photography as an almost universal hobby. During the 1920s and 1930s the Germans developed the 35mm film format which enabled Leitz and Zeiss to take the lead in camera design with their Leica and Contax models. Today they are highly prized by collectors who consider them to be Rolls Royces amongst cameras, while the huge range of Kodak products provides the enthusiast with hundreds of interesting and often inexpensive cameras of all types, colours and sizes to collect.

Above, left: A Meagher-type mahogany tailboard view camera with black bellows and barrel lens. *£1,500.*

Above, right: A small mahogany field view plate camera with rack-and-pinion focusing, adjustable rising front and f6 lens. *£130.*

Leitz: A Leica Standard 35mm camera No. 353299 with Leitz Elmar f3.5 5cm lens and leather case. *£200.*

Leitz: A black Leica III 35mm camera No. 148119 with Leitz Summar f2 5cm lens and a leather case. *£250.*

Leitz: A Leica IC 35mm camera No. 456045 with Leitz Elmar f3.5 5cm lens and viewfinder. *£250.*

Leitz: A Leica M2 35mm camera No. 971444 with Leitz Summicron f2 5cm lens, Leicameter MC and maker's leather case. *£400.*

Left: Houghton: A 'Ticka' pocket-watch style detective camera, with film and original sales box, for A. W. Gamage Ltd. Holborn, London. *£200.*

Below: Stirn: A concealed vest camera for six exposures. *£400.*

Above, left: An Ihagee Kine Exakta I camera with rectangular magnifier and Zeiss Tessar f3.5 5cm lens, *c.* 1940. *£150.*

Above, right: A black Zeiss Contax 1 35mm camera with Tessar f2.8 5cm lens, *c.* 1935. *£200.*

Right: Hasselblad, A 500 C 6 x 6cm SLR camera No. TH 48136 with roll film magazine No. TS 55123 and Zeiss Planar f2.8 80mm lens, No. 3468114, and Zeiss Sonnar f5.6 250mm lens No. 3193344, together with a quantity of Hasselblad accessories and equipment. *£1,500.*

Bottom, left: A 'Sanderson' mahogany and brass ¼-plate hand and stand camera with Zeiss lens in a Koilos shutter, *c.* 1900. *£250.*

Bottom, right: A 'Sanderson' mahogany and brass folding ¼-plate field camera with Clement and Gilmar lens, *c.* 1900. *£150.*

Right: An album of approximately 80 images, including military groups, Suez Canal, Delhi, Punjab, etc., *c.* 1890. *£50–80.*

Below: An album of approximately 80 images of India including temples and shrines, ruins, towns, elephants and types. £80–120.

Above: Julia Margaret Cameron. 'The Dedication', oval portrait of a young woman being handed a floral crown, inscribed 'From life registered photograph copyright Julia Margaret Cameron', mounted and framed, 6½ x 8¾in (16.25 x 22cm). *£300.*

Above: A black-and-white three-quarter length photographic portrait of the Duke and Duchess of Windsor, signed in ink 'Edward 1940', and 'Wallis Windsor', and signed in crayon in the margin, 'Beaton', 10 x 9in (26 x 23cm) contained in leather travelling frame. *£3,000–4,000.*

Right: F. Frith. 'The Pyramids of Dahshoor', albumen print, 15 x 18½in (38 x 47cm), mounted on card with printed title, signed in the negative, 'Frith 1858'. *£100–200.*

Far left: An Eastman Kodak Company No.2 stereo Brownie rollfilm camera, for 3.25 x 2.5in (8 x 6.25cm) exposure pairs, *c.* 1905. *£150.*

Left: A Witt Iloca Stereo II 35mm camera for 23 x 24mm pairs, with Ilitar f3.5 lenses and Prontor-S shutter, *c.* 1950. *£80.*

PRINTED EPHEMERA

The interest in printed ephemera dates back to the reign of Queen Victoria, and many clubs and exhibitions exist today specialising in the wide range of collecting categories within this field.

Postcard collecting is the second most popular hobby in Great Britain after stamp collecting, benefiting from numerous swap-meet events and monthly publications dealing with both old and modern cards. Most postcards produced before 1920 have some value; however, collectors tend to specialise in particular subjects or in cards of a certain age. For example, 'real photograph' cards are eagerly sought-after because they often cover local events such as floods, charabanc accidents, military parades etc.

Cigarette cards, available with most brands of tobacco since the 1890s, and becoming particularly popular in the 1930s, make for a surprisingly educational collecting hobby. Most sets of 25 or 50 cards issued by Players, Wills, and Churchman in the 1930s can still be obtained for less than £20. They feature a wide selection of subjects, including motorcars, football and cricket players, film and radio stars, military equipment, etc. Earlier sets of cards, because of their age and rarity, will usually cost the collector between £50 and £500 per set.

Autograph collecting takes many forms and is as popular now as it was in the late 19th century when Victorians collected the crests and signatures of leading politicians, clergymen and music-hall artistes. Today, the signatures of actors and actresses, pop stars and sporting heroes are more popular. The more famous personalities command the top prices. A signed photograph of Laurel and Hardy is worth up to £300; a signed letter from the 'Doctor' W. G. Grace, £50, and an autographed copy of John Lennon's 'A Spaniard in the Works', £300. Collectors should remember that many personalities and public figures employ either 'stamped' or 'secretarial' signatures, which are not authentic and are of little value.

Below: Raphael Tuck and Sons. Printed and pierced foldout novelty cards, including Old Mother Hubbard, A Visit to the Aquarium and scenes from Aladdin. *£10 each.*

Left: Six 'real photograph' American postcards of the Wild West including Col. 'Buffalo Bill' Cody and Red Indians. *£30 each.*

Below: Four transport postcards, including 'real photograph' vintage motorcars and two coloured hold-to-light shipping scenes. *£5 each.*

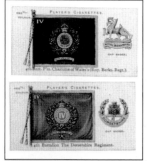

Left: Player's 'Regimental Colours and Cap-Badges', 1910, set of 50. *£25.*

Bottom left: Taddy's 'Autographs', 1912, set of 25. *£150.*

Below: F. & J. Smith's 'Famous Explorers', 1911, set of 50. *£200.*

Left: Taddy's 'Heraldry Series', 1911, set of 25. *£250.*

Bottom left: Player's 'Nature Series', 1908, set of 50. *£35.*

Below: Ogden's 'British Birds' Eggs', 1904, set of 50. *£40.*

AMERICAN CIGARETTE CARDS: *Right, clockwise from top left:* Allen & Ginter's 'Racing Colours of the World', 1888, set of 50, *£300.* Kinney's 'Navy Vessels of the World', 1889, set of 25, *£150.* Allen & Ginter's 'City Flags', 1888, set of 50, *£250.* Kimball's 'Fancy Bathers', 1889, set of 50, *£250.* Kinney's 'Famous Running Horses', 1890, set of 25, *£150.* Kimball's 'Beauties' (playing card inset), 1895, set of 52, *£300.* Duke's 'Postage Stamps', 1888, set of 50, *£350.* Allen & Ginter's 'American Indian Chiefs', 1888, set of 50, *£350.* Allen & Ginter's 'The World's Decorations', 1890, set of 50, *£350.* Allen & Ginter's 'Pirates of the Spanish Main', 1888, set of 50, *£450.*

Left: Carreras' 'The Science of Boxing', 1916, set of 50. *£40.*

Right: Ogden's 'Flags and Funnels of Leading Steamship Lines', 1906, set of 50. *£100.*

Left: Player's 'Badges and Flags of British Regiments', 1904, set of 50. *£60.*

Right: Wills' 'Musical Celebrities', 1911, set of 50. *£40.*

Far left pair: Gallaher's 'Woodland' series, 1912, set of 100. *£150.*

Near left pair: Wills' 'Time and Money', 1906, set of 50. *£40.*

Far left pair: R. & J. Lea's 'Old English Pottery and Porcelain', 1912, set of 50. *£55.*

Near left pair: Player's 'Victoria Cross', 1914, set of 25. *£20.*

Below: Raphael Tuck postcards. Two chromolithographic 'Kings & Queens of England' series of James II and Queen Anne, and two 'English Cathedrals' series of York Minster and Salisbury Cathedral; each with undivided backs, *c.* 1904. *£10 each.*

Above: Children's postcard subjects. *Clockwise from top left:* 'Faith', 'real photograph' French card. Coloured greetings card, published by M. M. (France). Coloured birthday greetings card with verse. British coloured 'real photograph' card with embossed border. *£1.50-3 each.*

Opposite: Four military postcards. *Clockwise from far left:* British anti-German card, *c.* 1914. Gale & Polden's 'Regimental Cap badges and buttons', 1915. 'Real photograph' 'Military Funeral Mill Hill' published by S. G. Allpress, Edgware, 1906. *£5-15 each.*

Right: Fantasy Head postcards. *£40-60 each.*

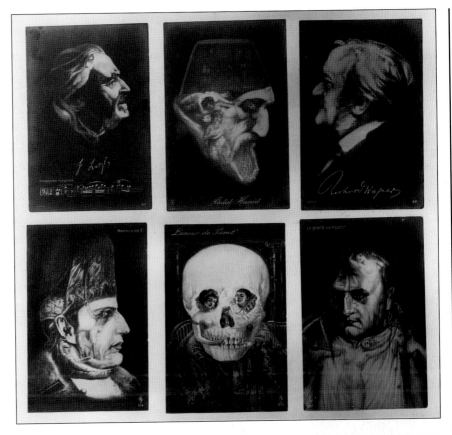

Below: Four anti-free trade John Bull postcards by Arthur Moreland, published by C. W. Faulkner & Co. London. *£20 each.*

Right: Charles Chaplin, from an album of autographs including Stan Laurel, Malcolm Campbell, Harry Lauder, Dennis Wheatley, George Bernard Shaw, Julie Andrews, Jimmy Edwards, Clark Gable, Jack Hylton, Gladys Cooper, Noel Coward, Ivor Novello, Cary Grant, Gracie Fields, Tony Webster, Chaz Chase, Maurice Chevalier, Coco the Clown, etc. £400-600.

Left: A banjo by Barnes & Mullins (London), bearing 21 ink signatures on the calf-skin membrane including Agatha Christie, Jack Buchanan, Mussolini, D'Oyly Carte, Ivor Novello, Trotsky, Edward (Prince of Wales), Noel Coward, Lloyd George, Oswald Mosley, Sophie Tucker and Stanley Baldwin. £400-600.

Below: An example from an album of 170 pages of letters, envelopes, autographs scraps and samples of handwriting of Georgian and Victorian royalty, statesmen, politicians, clergy and public figures, including Gladstone, Palmerston, Pitt, Thackeray, Queen Victoria, Walpole, Wellington and others, with two indices, £320.

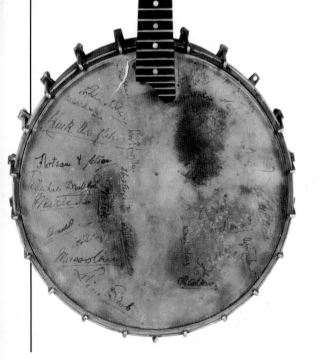

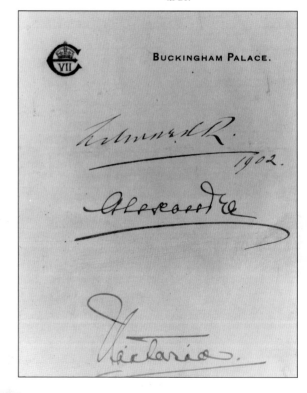

Above: Duke and Duchess of Windsor.
A Christmas card bearing a monogram and portrait print of the couple and signed in ink 'Wallis & Edward', 5½ x 8in (14 x 20.5cm). *£500-800.*

Left: Walt Disney. A pen-and-watercolour cartoon depicting Mickey Mouse and Donald Duck playing cricket whilst Minnie Mouse, Pluto and the rabbit look on; Walt Disney's signature in ink, 7¼ x 5in (14.5 x 10cm). *£400-600.*

Above: A collection
of German
chromolithographic stand-
up Christmas cards, *c.* 1907.
£30-50 each.

Right: Edwardian
chromolithographed
postcards by Faulkner.
£10 each.

DAILY SKETCH
AND DAILY GRAPHIC
Coronation Souvenir
TUESDAY, JUNE 2, 1953   2d.

GOD BLESS HER ON THIS DAY

Left: The Coronation souvenir edition (2 June 1953) of the 'Daily Sketch and Daily Graphic'. *£30-50.*

Right: A chromolithographic tea box for Mazawattee Tea with designs by Louis Wain, *c.* 1930. *£60.*

QUILTS

The word quilt stems from the Latin *culcita*, meaning cushion or pad — the wadding between the two sheets of fabric usually found in a quilt. Although 19th-century American quilts are well established in the collecting market, English and Welsh quilts are also fascinating, and often the collector is pleasantly surprised by their affordability. 'Durham' (made in the 19th and early 20th centuries in mining areas of the north of England) and country quilts can be found for as little as £100 (although particularly well-executed examples can cost at least twice that).

Victorian patchwork quilts are another good investment; bright and cheerful, they can be bought for about £200. A finely-worked example is made of thousands of tiny hexagonal patches from the household's rag-bag — a wonderful mixture of furnishing fabrics, velvets, and printed and plain cottons. Some may even have the original templates attached — an interesting and useful way to date the quilt, as they were often made from the household's letters, bills and receipts.

A mid-19th century 'grandmother's' flower-garden-pattern quilt containing some 18th-century material, 112 x 108in (280 x 270cm). *£950.*

A 'double wedding ring'-pattern 1920s American quilt, 110 x 106in (275 x 265cm). *£450.*

RADIOS

When the British Broadcasting Corporation began transmitting a regular service from London in the 1920s, the modern radio was born. Today it is difficult to imagine life without a radio or television set, and so it is not surprising that listening to the 'wireless' became a favourite pastime. News, sport and music programmes were soon being broadcast to the front rooms of houses around the country via radio sets that are now thought of by many collectors as works of art.

The wooden and bakelite-case examples of the 1930s reflected the Art Deco style of the day.

Household names such as Philips, Pye, GEC, Ekco and Bush produced radios from the earliest days, and employed designers who styled the cases to mimic gothic architecture, clock cases, motorcar grilles and even toasters!

Old radios are still plentiful and fairly inexpensive; however, condition is important, as restoration is both difficult and costly. Old wiring and tired or broken valves are expensive to replace, while damaged or scratched cases may be impossible to return to their former glory. Good radios can be obtained from auction or dealers for under £100.

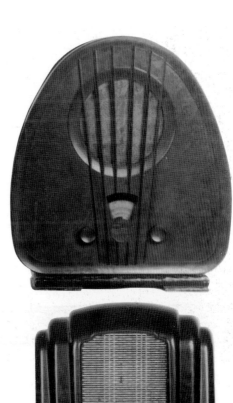

Above: A Mende radio, type 180W, *c.* 1940, curved brown bakelite case with circular dial above three knobs, 17¾in (45cm) high. *£100–150.*

Above, right: A Philips radio, type 834A, 1929, bakelite front on black wooden base, 17¾in (45cm) high. *£150–200.*

Right: A Ferranti Ltd. radio, type 145E, *c.* 1940, black bakelite case, meshed grille above square dial, 18in (46cm) high. *£150–250.*

Far left: Wells Coates UK. An Ekco radio, type A.D.75, designed for E. K. Cole Ltd., *c.* 1935, serial No. 48851, circular brown bakelite case, 14¼in (36cm) diam. *£400–600.*

Left: A fine Senora radio, type Excellence 301, 1946, 'Cadillac' styled in bakelite case with metal trim, 11in (28cm) high, 18¼in (46.2cm) wide. *£500–700.*

Right: A Murphy Radio Ltd. radio, type SAD 94, serial No. 117282, black bakelite with vertical speaker grille, 14in (34.5cm) high. *£200–300.*

Below: An Integra radio, type LT 3750, 1940s, rectangular brown bakelite case, 17in (43.5cm) high. *£80–120.*

Below: A Philips type 2003 speaker (the first to be produced in bakelite), 1925, brown mottled bakelite of circular form, 18in (45.5cm) diam., 19in (48cm) high. *£250–450.*

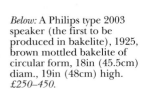

RAILWAY BYGONES

Since the demise of the steam locomotive, railway preservation societies, as well as individual collectors of railway bygones have proliferated. Locomotives have been dismantled for souvenirs, and it is not unusual to find a £2,000 price-tag on a nameplate from an important engine. Rolling-stock and goods yards provided a happy hunting ground for makers' plates (up to £500), wagon plates (£30), lamps (£50-200), station nameplates (up to £500), and even station benches (up to £600). Crockery and silver plate from railway hotels and dining cars commonly change hands for £50 or so a piece. Although the supply of uniforms, hats, watches and signals is becoming scarcer, the collector can turn to printed ephemera such as headed notepaper, tickets and timetables. More decorative pieces include period postcards (up to £10), prints and photographs (around £100) and, of course, paintings, which can cost thousands of pounds.

The biggest growth area of recent years has been posters, which appeal to many besides railway buffs. They can cost £300-700 for a pre-British Rail-era poster (many of which advertise popular holiday resorts with the railway as the suggested means of transport).

Left: An unsigned etching of Waterloo station, *c.* 1925. *£85.*

Above: A Staffordshire pottery mug printed in black and decorated in colour of an early railway scene, *c.* 1850, 4in (10cm) high. *£250.*

SAMPLERS

Samplers originated in the 16th century when they were used to record designs before the advent of printing. The word 'sampler' or 'exampler', derives from the French *essamplaire*, meaning work to be copied.

Samplers were most commonly thought of as a way of teaching children different sewing techniques whilst encouraging filial obedience and respect for God. There are many different types to look out for: darning samplers to practise marking household linen, plain sewing samplers for learning how to make clothes, map samplers to teach geography, and others to record family events.

The style of the needlework and the layout evolved through the centuries. Seventeenth-century samplers were long and narrow in shape, worked either on natural-coloured linen in silk threads, or in silks of many colours. Cutwork is often found in examples from the early 17th century: the techniques include darning on a net foundation and buttonholing around raw edges when the threads have been cut away.

Eighteenth-century samplers were squarer in shape, the patterns becoming more symmetrical or regular. By the 19th century, sampler pattern books were widely available, with the result that the designs became increasingly alike – schoolgirl exercises with little originality. The Arts and Crafts movement at the end of the 19th century encouraged samplers which paid more attention to stitch technique than overall pattern.

As the vegetable-dyed threads are susceptible to fading, and the base cloths prone to mildew, samplers are best kept in dry conditions away from direct sunlight. When buying antique samplers, choose those where the embroidery threads have retained their colour and the base cloth is clean and intact.

Needlework sampler commemorating the Silver Jubilee, dated 1951, 12 x 16in (30 x 40cm). *£60-100.*

A finely worked needlework sampler of a four-line verse above a chinoiserie pagoda and enclosure, small figures and birds above a small vignette of Adam and Eve flanking the Tree of Knowledge, by Mary Worster, dated September 1794, 12 x 15in (30 x 37.5cm). *£700-900.*

Above: A needlework sampler by Martha Goodall, aged 8, dated 1827, of Adam and Eve and the Tree of Knowledge above a three-storey house surrounded by small animals and birds, 12 x 14in (30 x 35cm). *£400-500.*

Below: A mid-19th-century needlework sampler of 'St Paul's Church' by Ellen Virgin, aged 11, finished April 9th 1841, the work executed in fine cross stitch depicting St Paul's Cathedral surrounded by stylised trees, baskets of flowers, stars and birds, 19¼ x 15in (49 x 38cm). *£200-400.*

Above: A large mid-19th-century needlework sampler by Alice Buckley, dated 1841, of the Bluecoat School in Oldham, Lancashire, with a six-line verse, together with floral sprays with a fruiting border, 19¼ x 17¾in (49 x 45cm). *£250-300.*

Below: A late 19th-century needlework sampler by Sarah Hemsley of Bexley Heath, Kent, dated April 21st 1894, worked in fine coloured silks of alphabets and floral borders above animals and a small two-storey house in parkland, 16½ x 13in (42 x 33cm), unframed. *£150-250.*

SCIENTIFIC INSTRUMENTS

Although 18th-century and earlier scientific instruments can be very expensive indeed, it is still possible to put together a collection of 19th- and early 20th-century pieces for reasonable amounts of money.

Optical instruments include, for example, hand-held refracting telescopes at about £30 (£2,000 for a large brass version with altazimuth mounts). Reflecting telescopes (usually earlier than refracting models) normally start at £600. A monocular microscope can cost as little as £30, whereas a large and complicated binocular microscope will be over £700.

As for measuring instruments, brass theodolites are sought-after, and a fairly simple example, *c.* 1914, will fetch £40 at auction, whereas a more complicated transit theodolite might realise £500. Pocket sextants and clinometers also make attractive and affordable collectables.

Scientific balances in a glass case can cost as little as £25, whereas large brass, mahogany and marble shop scales may well be £400. Coin balances, apothecaries' balances and opium scales can all be bought relatively cheaply, as can the attractive Sykes hydrometer (for measuring the specific gravity of liquid), £25 being a fairly typical price.

A mid-19th-century orrery signed 'Newton & Co., Opticians to the Queen, 3 Fleet Street, London'; the circular wooden base is applied with hand-coloured paper showing the months and various stars: the sun represented by a gilt brass sphere, ivory planets on brass arms and a lunarium, the earth with coloured paper gores, Mars with two moons, Jupiter four, Saturn eight, Uranus four and Neptune one. It is operated by a turned ivory handle; base 17in (43cm) diam., in original wooden travelling box with Newton's trade label in the lid. *£10,000.*

Below: A late 18th-century brass-compound monocular microscope signed 'B. Martin, Invt, London' on the body tube, located on an adjustable arm from the vertical baluster pillar, focusing in the Cuff manner by sliding pillar and sleeve with long fine-focus screw, folding tripod stand, in a red velvet-lined fishskin-covered case with a range of accessories and slides, 10in (26cm). £1,500–2,000.

Left: George Adams. A rare set of silver 18th-century drawing instruments, the lid containing a folding sector rule and square, signed 'Improved and made by G. Adams, Math. Instrum. Maker to His Royal Highness the Prince of Wales, in Fleet Street, London', a scale rule, signed 'Made by G. Adams in Fleet Street, London', both sides engraved with scales, a parallel rule, a silver and ivory folding square, the main velvet-lined tray with numerous instruments including proportional dividers in a shagreen case with silvered clasps and lock, 9in (23cm). £18,000.

Above: Goldsmiths and Silversmiths Company: a tortoiseshell and silver-mounted postal scale, rectangular with scroll and shell-chased applied silver mounts, with silver weighting mechanism, London, 1902, 7¼ x 5½in (18.5 x 14cm). *£1,500.*

Above: A rare miniature lacquered brass sextant, inset silver scale to the arc, vernier scale and magnifier to the index arm, the ivory-handled frame with adjustable telescope mounting socket; with two telescopes and various accessories in a shaped mahogany box, 4½ in (12cm) radius. *£600–900.*

Above: A matched pair of early Victorian terrestrial and celestial globes, by Newtons, on ring-turned columns and downswept tripod supports, the celestial globe distressed, 39in (99cm) high. *£5,000.*

Below: A radioactive sample contained in a miniature oak coffin (to represent a lead coffin) inscribed 'Einstein to Finniston — Theory and Experiment', presented to Sir Monty Finniston in 1958 by the Metallurgy Division at Harwell. *£500–700.*

SCREENS

A screen's main function was to block draughts — invaluable in an age before adequate insulation or central heating! Historical evidence suggests that screens date from the late 16th century and declined in use from the 1920s. They were made in a variety of materials, including tapestry, Chinese lacquer, velvet, silk and paper. Wooden screens were often embellished with marquetry, carving and fretwork and, in Edwardian times, sometimes contained panes of bevelled glass. During the early 19th century, for example, highly ornate frames enclosed silk panels, and during the 18th century artists were commissioned to paint pastoral or sporting scenes on screens made by leading cabinet-makers of the day such as Chippendale and Hepplewhite.

During the 19th century screens became a popular place to paste on pictures (often of celebrities and royalty), and these scrapwork screens now afford us a fascinating record of Victorian personalities.

A late 18th-century Dutch painted four-fold screen, the main scene depicting oriental figures, 52in (132cm) wide. £460.

A painted four-fold screen, the folds decorated in polychrome on a cream field with an arrangement of exotic birds and flowering shrubs around a pool, 81 x 24in (206 x 61cm) each fold. £4,500.

A four-fold painted leather screen, after Watteau, the arched panels painted with a romantic scene of a gentleman wooing a maiden, 19th-century English, 88in (224cm) wide. £800.

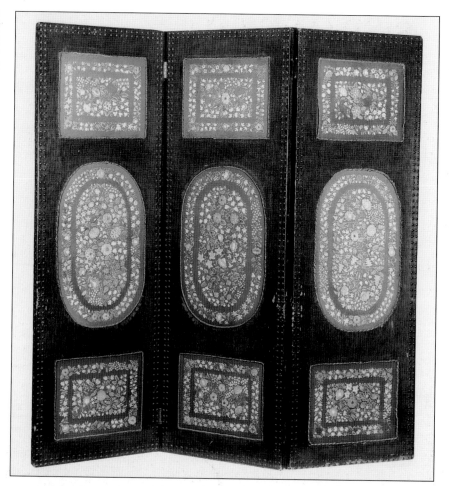

A rare Huron moosehead embroidered screen, 1840-50, comprising nine decorated panels, each with delicate floral patterns embroidered on a felt backing, the large centred oval panels on a red ground, the screen of green velvet, 72in (183cm). *£3,000.*

A chinoiserie four-fold screen, the folds painted on silk with oriental landscape of figures amongst pavilions, rocks and gnarled trees, 75½ x 24⅛in (192 x 62cm) each fold. *£750.*

SCRIMSHAW

Most enthusiasts of nauticalia will have at least one piece of scrimshaw in their collection. It is a term used to describe the carved walrus tusks, whalebone, and sometimes shells, executed by sailors on 19th-century whaling ships and also much favoured by French prisoners-of-war in England during the Napoleonic wars as a way to pass the time. Herman Melville, the author of *Moby Dick,* described the American whalers' 'dentistical-looking implements specially intended for the skrimshandering business.' But, he added, ' . . . in general they toil with their jack-knives alone.'

The origin of the word is uncertain, and although one theory is that it derives from the name of an admiral renowned for his carving, there is no real evidence.

Carved whales' teeth or bone carving of the 19th century is the most sought-after. The uninitiated collector should be wary of modern plastic replicas depicting American whalers or sailors and their 'true loves' — favourite themes of scrimshawists in the last century. They can be surprisingly realistic, and the only acid test (applying a flame to see if you can smell burning plastic) is not one much appreciated by dealers.

Left: An interesting and probably unique scrimshaw 'bell', formed as a three-tier cruciform wooden frame, united by woven coloured silk threads and hung with giltwood bells, signed 'Sumner Yarmouth 1836', assembled within a cylindrical glass jar and made to revolve via the wooden bung, 8¼in (21cm). *£100–200.*

Below: A French Napoleonic prisoner-of-war bone domino and cribbage set, carved with geometrical motifs, the sliding cover and sides with painted card panels depicting period figures and landscape scenes, and containing a collection of carved dominoes. *£280.*

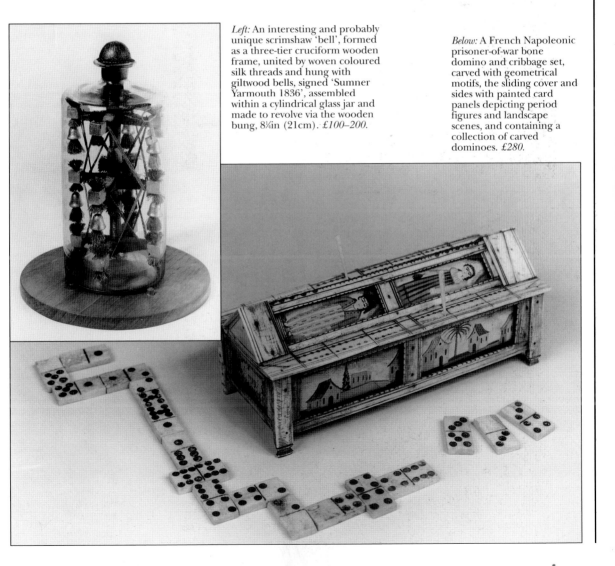

SEWING COLLECTABLES

Hand-sewing collectables encompass a wide range of 17th-, 18th- and 19th-century items including sewing and needle cases, thimbles, pin-cushions, scissors and tape measures. Occasionally one finds sewing boxes (sometimes on stands). The general area can also include wool-working implements.

In Victorian Britain it was considered polite for ladies to take their embroidery to social gatherings, and dainty sewing accessories were manufactured for them. A sewing set or 'ladies' companion' consisted of a decorated leather box containing fine implements: scissors, thimble, pencil, tweezers, needle case and a scent bottle. More decorative still were 'châtelaines' which hung from a belt and from which sewing implements were attached by chains. Top-quality châtelaines were highly ornate and often made from silver.

With the advent of mechanisation in the 19th century, domestic and commercial sewing machines were introduced, and they and their assorted paraphernalia such as bobbins are now also collected.

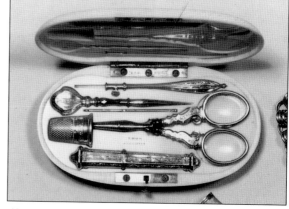

Above: A French nécessaire, the oval ivory case with hinged cover revealing a needle case, scissors, thimble, a needle holder, an unpicker and a needle, *c.* 1870. £300-400.

Right: An oak wool winder, the twin reels with adjustable settings, 39in (99cm) high. £50.

Left: A George III satinwood work box, the rectangular hinged cover inlaid with a central flowerhead medallion, opening to reveal a fitted interior with partitions and covered compartments, with drawer below, the whole with tulipwood banding, 12in (30.5cm) wide (with numerous ivory fitments). £1,300.

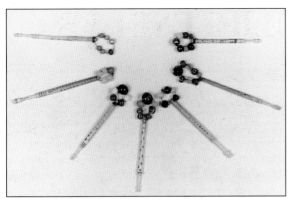

Above: A collection of named and initialled bone bobbins, including David Headland and Ann Gammons. *£50-100.*

Above: A Victorian papier-mâché and parcel-gilt sewing table, inlaid with mother-of-pearl, the octagonal top enclosing a fitted interior, above a tapered faceted stem with a lappet-leaf collar, on a circular plinth and scroll feet, 18½ in (47cm) wide. *£500.*

Right: An Art Deco inlaid walnut sewing cabinet on stand, of hexagonal coffer form, the hinged cover lifting to reveal fitted compartments with a drawer flanked by two slides, on four elongated square-section legs, 42in (70cm) high, 18in (46cm) wide. *£1,000.*

Above: A fine Bavarian fruitwood spinning wheel, *c.* 1700, the frame finely turned with multiple balusters, the wheel and footboard applied with acorns and leaves, 51in (129cm). *£800-1,200.*

SILHOUETTES

Profilists employed several methods to produce their work, from simple cut-out black card mounted on board, to those techniques also employed by skilled miniaturists. Painted silhouettes used the media of watercolour or Indian ink on card, or a mixture of pine-soot and beer on glass or plaster ovals.

The most common composition in silhouette portraiture, which flourished from 1770 to 1860, depicts the head and shoulders in profile. Groups of people and scenes were also used as subjects throughout the history of silhouetting, although from 1830, single full-length figures became predominant. Artists usually pasted their trade-labels on the backs of frames, thus making identification relatively simple.

Among the top profilists were John Miers and Mrs Isabella Beetham, both working in London; William Hamlet Senior, who practised in Bath between 1780 and 1815, and Charles Rosenberg, also based in Bath. Each developed his or her own style: for example, Hamlet highlighted clothing details with overpainted gold-leaf, whilst Mrs Beetham's silhouettes were often bordered with patterns of gold foil.

Left: An early 19th-century oval silhouette of Mrs William Lane, in wooden oval frame. *£420.*

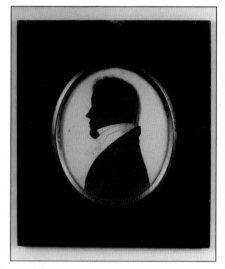

Right: A early 19th-century oval silhouette of a young gentleman, in an ebonised-wood frame. *£190.*

Far left: 'Father and Son', by Auguste Edouard, *c.* 1830, with watercolour-wash background. *£150.*

Left: A modern (*c.* 1980) silhouette of the 'Captain's Table'. *£20.*

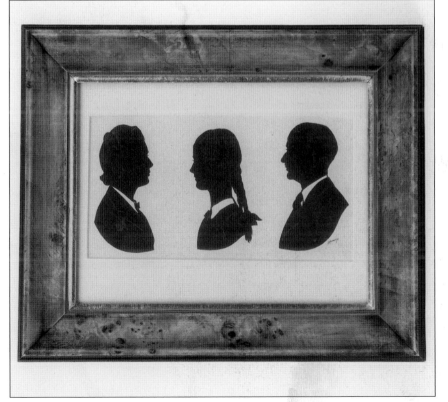

Above, centre: A painted silhouette of George IV, black-lacquered papier-mâché frame applied with the royal coat of arms. *£60-80.*

Above, left and right: A pair of painted silhouettes of the Duke of York and the Duke of Sussex, *c.* 1824. *£100-150.*

Left: A family group by Oakley of Edinburgh, *c.* 1947. *£40.*

SMOKING COLLECTABLES

Tobacco was first introduced to England by Sir Walter Raleigh in 1584 during the reign of Queen Elizabeth, and very quickly the habit of smoking tobacco became universally popular; it remained so until the introduction of the cigarette in the 1880s.

Porcelain pipes first appeared in Germany during the 1760s. They had slender vertical mouthpieces, long upright bowls and painted decoration. Again, the bowls were sometimes moulded in the form of heads, and these, together with examples produced by the Meissen factory, are eagerly collected. Meerschaum pipes, usually of German manufacture, became available in Britain in the 1750s, and by the 1830s the early Victorian smokers fully appreciated the elaborately carved pipes that are so widely collected today.

Cigarettes first appeared in Europe in the 1860s and, as their popularity grew, so the number of associated accessories increased, so that by the early 20th century ornate cigarette holders, cases, lighters and ashtrays were available to the discerning smoker.

Above: A 19th-century steel and mahogany tobacco cutter, the base carved as an alligator with polychrome decoration, the steel blade attached to a carved floral bocage, dated May 1876, 14¼in (36cm) long. £290.

Right: A painted wooden snuff or tobacco figure of a Scotsman, standing wearing a red tunic, tartan sash and kilt, his right hand aloft holding a pinch of snuff, his left hand with a snuff mull, on a canted stepped plinth, 37½in (95.5cm) high, 19th century. £1,700.

Above: J. B. Hennell: An unusual 'Elephant' cigar lighter, 2¾in (7cm), with pull-off cover and detachable mahout. London. £1,300.

Right: A lacquer cigar box with hinged cover and dropped side decorated in gold hiramakie and takamakie, with a cockerel by a stream, a basket of flowers and fan, the interior decorated with butterflies and six fitted trays all on a nashiji ground, 12 x 7½in (30.5 x 19cm), Meiji period. £200.

Above: A Dunhill silver-plated compact in the form of a lighter, rectangular with panels of engine-turning, hinged to one side to reveal mirrored compartment, with integral scent bottle to one side and lipstick to the other, the simulated lighter mechanism containing an eye-liner pencil, stamped 'Dunhill', with registration and patent numbers stamped to the base. *£400–600.*

Right: A Russian white-metal cigarette case 4½ x 3½in (11.5 x 8.9cm), rectangular, the hinged cover decorated with an allegorical figure representing industry on one side and a group of rustic figures on the other, with cabochon ruby thumbpiece. *£260.*

Left: A silver-gilt Dunhill Unique lighter, the engine-turned body with a pointed enamel plaque to the front depicting a standing naked woman, fitted case. *£1,000.*

Below: Continental white-metal cigarette case, 3½ x 3¼in (8.9 x 8.3cm), the hinged cover with polychromatic enamel depicting a naked nymph, *c.* 1900. *£750.*

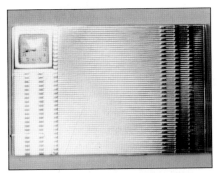

Left: An unusual cigarette case-cum-lighter and watch, the reeded rectangular body with gilt decoration and gilt push-button thumbpiece, the lighter self-contained, the nickel lever escapement with square silvered dial, commemorative inscription to gilt interior, London 1940, by the Goldsmiths and Silversmiths Company. *£300–500.*

Left: top row, left to right: A Continental white-metal and enamelled cigarette case, *c. 1910. £300-500.* A Continental silver-and-enamel cigarette case, *c. 1900. £300-400.* A German white-metal and enamel cigarette box, *c.* 1910. *£300-500. Bottom row, left to right:* A Continental silver-plated cigarette case, *c. 1900. £100-160.* A Japanese cigarette case with double-hinged cover, *c. 1910. £70-100.* An inlaid Japanese cigarette case, *c. 1910. £70-100.*

Left-hand side, top to bottom:
A carved meerschaum pipe, the bowl supported by a gentleman's left hand, amber mouthpiece. £70.

An elaborately carved meerschaum cheroot holder, modelled as a fashionable young lady at rest raising a glass to her lips, with white-metal mount and amber mouthpiece, (cased). £100.

A carved meerschaum pipe, modelled as a lady wearing a feathered bonnet, with mouthpiece, (cased). £150.

A carved meerschaum pipe, modelled as a human skull above crossed bones, with stem, (cased). £60.

Right-hand side, top to bottom:
A carved meerschaum pipe, modelled as a man with flowing beard wearing a tasselled cap, with white-metal mount and amber stem, (cased). £50.

A carved meerschaum cheroot holder, modelled as a fashionably dressed girl seated with a basket of flowers, with mouthpiece, (cased). £50.

A carved meerschaum cheroot holder, modelled as a lion impaled upon the amber mouthpiece modelled as a spear, (cased). £100.

A carved meerschaum pipe, the bowl carved as a bearded Saracen wearing traditional head-dress, with elaborate white metal mount, amber mouthpiece, (cased). £100.

A carved meerschaum cheroot with a young lady, a cherub and a cat, (cased). £30.

Left: A Cigaretto cigarette vending all-win machine, the rectangular wood case with cast-metal controls, 1d. coin chute, the spiralling ball chute and seven ball cups upon red, yellow, green and blue sunburst background, 25in (64cm) high. £280.

SNUFF BOXES & BOTTLES

During the mid-17th century the court of Louis XIII of France promoted the fashion for snuff-taking over tobacco smoking, and Charles II introduced the new habit to England on his accession to the throne. Snuff-taking enjoyed great popularity until the introduction of cigars and cigarettes in the mid-19th century.

Snuff boxes were produced in many shapes and sizes, and the materials used in their construction included wood, papier-mâché, ivory, tortoiseshell and silver. Most examples that the collector will encounter were made of wood, including the popular 'shoe-boxes', coffins, barrels, hats and boats.

Papier-mâché snuff boxes were usually square or round, with hinged lids, and were often painted or printed with decorative scenes. Silver was reserved for high-quality examples, as was ivory and tortoiseshell.

Prices for snuff boxes depend on the age and sophistication of each example, but as a rule they can be obtained for as little as £20 for a standard wooden box, to several hundred pounds for an ornate silver and tortoiseshell specimen.

Snuff bottles were made from a wide range of materials, including jade, porcelain, agate and amethyst, and many can be had for under £200.

Above and right: A snuff box presented to Dr H. Hoadly by William Hogarth. The cover *(right)* shows characters from the Commedia dell'Arte. A sliding panel reveals a typically Hogarthian scene painted on the inside *(above)*, 3 x 2¼in (7.5 x 5.6cm). *£1,500-2,000.*

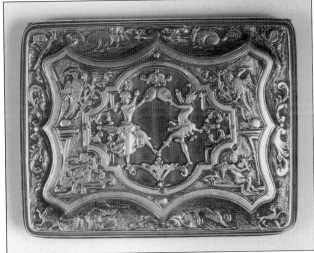

SNUFF BOTTLES:
Above, clockwise from top left:
A large burganté bottle, possibly Japanese. *£140.*

A metal and enamelled bottle of meiping form, 19th century. *£120.*

A bottle of celadon jade. *£140.*

An 'inside painted' bottle in an oriental style. *£95.*

A late 18th-century red glass example. *£170.*

An early 19th-century glass overlay specimen. *£180.*

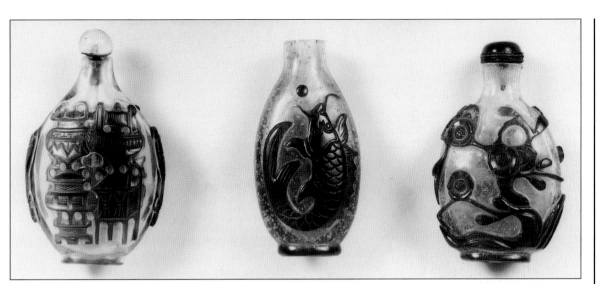

Above: Three 19th-century glass overlay snuff bottles. *£110-180 each.*

Above: A mid-19th-century German papier-mâché snuff box. *£420.*

Right: A French tortoiseshell snuff box, *c.* 1800. *£320.*

SPOONS

Spoons (except those made before about 1700) offer an affordable way to collect silver. The 18th century saw the production of Hanoverian and Old English patterned tea and coffee spoons, the former made from thin sheet silver and often incompletely marked, the latter, on the other hand, were fully marked.

Victorian teaspoons were often made with individual cases and are usually sold in sets which include sugar tongs. 'Apostle' spoons were, and are, very popular, and although they are not particularly rare, it is difficult to find them in pristine condition as they were made from thin-gauge silver. Souvenir spoons were also popular in the 19th century, and many were decorated with armorial terminals or with enamelled or engraved bowls.

Between 1880 and 1910 spoons were often stamped or chased with swirling designs which often incorporated enamelling, and those made by Liberty & Co. are particularly highly prized today.

Caddy spoons generally had shell-shaped bowls, while other popular shapes were acorns, thistles and horses' hooves, all deeply moulded to contain a good measure of tea.

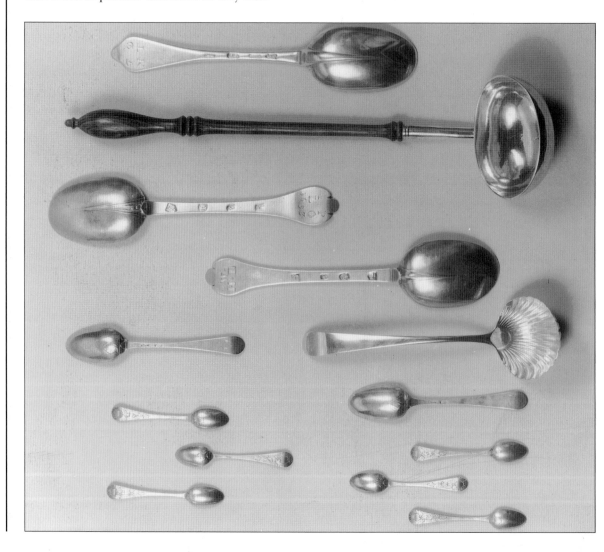

Far left: A William IV fiddle-pattern caddy spoon by Benoni Stephens, London, 1834. £40.

Left: A William IV fiddle-pattern caddy spoon by William Bateman, London, 1834. £45.

Below, from top:
A pair of George III Old English pattern serving spoons, by John Power, Dublin, 1802. £160.

A pair of George III Old English pattern serving spoons, Dublin, 1795. £260.

Opposite, from top:
A Queen Anne rat-tail spoon by Henry Greene, London, 1703. £140.

A George II toddy ladle, *c.* 1740. £110.

A pair of William and Mary rat-tail spoons by William Matthews II, London, 1694. £170.

A Georgian scallop-bowl ladle, *c.* 1760. £110.

Two George III Masonic picture-back teaspoons by William Cripps, London, 1760. £120.

A set of six George II shell-backed snuff spoons perhaps by William Cripps, London, *c.* 1760. £240.

Right: A Liberty & Co. silver George V Coronation spoon, Birmingham hallmarks for 1910. £300-500.

Above: A caddy spoon, Birmingham, 1898. £35.

Above: A Victorian fiddle-pattern caddy spoon, possibly by Wm. Smiley, London, 1857. £40.

SPORTING BYGONES

The passion for collecting sporting items seems to be a characteristically British one and dates from the 18th century when golf, cricket, pugilism and, of course, equestrian sports became firmly established as national enthusiasms. Reflecting the often elevated social status of their patrons, these sports in particular are widely represented in painting, silver and gold objects and fashionable ceramic wares. In contrast, soccer and coarse fishing (as distinct from the more 'aristocratic' pastime of fly-fishing), although hugely popular, are rarely found represented in 'fine art'. Whereas it is fairly common to discover silver toast-racks with dividers modelled as crossed golf clubs, or Lambeth stoneware pieces decorated with gentlemen cricketers, soccer's medium, for example, tends to be the rather humbler cigarette card.

There is a huge amount of sporting memorabilia which embraces prints, equipment, photographs, printed ephemera including autographs, and a considerable diversity of books ranging from memoirs to those of the 'improve-your-game' genre.

Below: J. C. Winter: Harry Vardon, oil on board, 8 x 5⅞in (20.5 x 15cm) framed. £200–300.

Upper left: Emmwood: Caricature montage of golfers Jack Nicklaus, Lee Trevino, Arnold Palmer, Tony Jacklin, Roberto de Vincenzo, Gary Player, Billy Casper and Peter Thompson, signed in ink, ink and wash on board, 20½ x 15in (52 x 38cm). £80–120.

Lower left: Schoenhut's Indoor Golf Set No. G/10, comprising 'Tommy Green' golf balls, golf clubs, bunkers, water hazard, etc., boxed, and set No. G/8 containing one 'Sissie Lofter' club, boxed. £100–150.

Right: A figure of a golfer, 12¼in (31cm) high, the amusingly modelled figure depicted with a club in hand having just played a stroke, on rectangular plinth, stamped '925' and signed 'Mark Nil'. £260.

Above: 'Body-Line' tour 1932-33: a mounted photograph of the R. M. S. Orontes, signed in ink in the margin by 10 members of the MCC touring side of Australia, 8¾ x 9¾in (20 x 24.5cm). £100-150.

Above, centre: 'The Tout' (P.R.G. Buchanan): A pencil-and-watercolour cartoon relating to the Stechworth Cricket Club entitled 'Calling all local Don Bradmans', 20in (50cm), signed and dated 1950. £150-200.

Above, right: Roy Ullyett: 'King Cricket', a sporting cartoon of Gary Sobers, pen, crayon and gouache, signed, 12 x 17½in (30.5 x 44cm). £200-300.

Right: After Kinsella: 'The Hope of His Side', oil on canvas, signed F. Vitale, 14½ x 9¾ in (37 x 25cm). £180.

Below: A pair of decorated presentation sculls with leather buttons presented to G. C. Owen, Trinity Hall Boat Club, Holland-Boat, length 58⅛in (149cm), with 11in (28cm) blades. £100-150.

Left: A pair of cricketers, one depicting a bowler wearing a rounded cap, the other depicting a batsman, holding a bat in both hands before stumps, both on oval gilt-lined bases, height 14in (36cm), c. 1865. £1,600.

Next page, bottom left: Squire: 'The Oarsman taking the Strain', watercolour on board, 22½ x 18in (57 x 45.5cm), overmounted. £80-120.

Above: H. L. Rolfe, 'Still Life of Salmon', oil on canvas, signed, dated and framed 29 x 17in (74 x 43cm). *£3,800.*

Left: A rare Hardy 3⅜in (9.4cm) wide brass drum Uniqua, with smooth brass foot, single ivory handle, stamped with 'Rod in Hand' logo to backplate. *£800.*

Below: A papier-mâché snuff box with angling scene, 'OH THE JOYS OF ANGLING, Why the duce don't you mind what you 'R at?' *£300.*

Above: A powan, mounted in a bow-fronted case, inscribed 'Powan Weight 11¼ ozs. Caught by Fred Buller, Loch Lomond Feb 1968', 1½in (3.75cm) wide. *£190.*

Below: A British record zander, mounted in a gilt-lined case, inscribed 'British Record Zander. Caught by Bill Chillingworth, Gt. Ouse, Relief Channel, Downham Market, Feb 21st 1971', 59½in (148.75cm) wide. *£800.*

Above: A lacquered papier-mâché tray, painted with racehorse and jockey, within a border of trailing gilt foliage, 27½in (70cm) wide. *£150.*

Above: A bronze racing group of two horses with jockeys brandishing crops, in mid-action jumping over a fence, upon octagonal base, bears signature 'Bonheur', 23in (58cm) tall. *£400-600.*

Right: An American 'What the butler saw' peep show machine, with 'The Artist and his Model' film strip, the upright oak case upon cast-metal cabriole lion's paw feet, display poster to the top, 50in high (127cm), stamped inside 2012, with Mike Munves Corp supplier's, plaque beside viewer. *£1,300.*

Far right: A Mill's High Top Cowboy one-arm bandit fruit machine, with 6d coin chute and mystery payout function, the body of a wood and plaster polychrome one-armed cowboy, with gun-arm working the machine, 72in (182cm) high. *£1,700.*

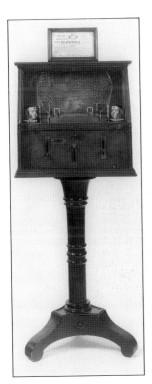

Right: A Genco official baseball pintable, with external wooden rails, the play field depicting two printed basketball players and a third in cast metal, the ball chute mounted with cast-metal batsman, the wooden casting with ebonised trim, marked with an American eagle on a shield inscribed 'N.R.A. member: We do our part'. *£480.*

Left: A. W. Haydon & Company (Islington) automatic blow-ball game for two players. One old penny sets a ball in play and two clown heads direct the ball by means of pumped air at a speed and strength controlled by each player. The stained-wood case with brass fittings. *£3,500.*

Above: A Bally Fireball pinball table, marked on back 'Midway Manufacturing Corp., Franklin Pk., Ill., U.S.A. 60131 A Bally Company'. *£420.*

STEVENGRAPHS

Stevengraphs are decorative woven silk pictures produced by Thomas Stevens (and later by his two sons) in Coventry between 1862 and 1938. They are usually colourful, with an almost three-dimensional quality. Stevens' silk pictures were inexpensive and immediately popular in their day. The different types can be divided into three categories — pictures, postcards and bookmarks.

The pictures were fitted into simple, titled, cardboard mounts, ready for framing. They depicted popular subjects such as coursing, fox-hunting and horse racing, as well as international trade exhibitions. Stevens would set up portable looms at these exhibitions where visitors were able to watch the pictures being woven and were then invited to buy them.

About 1900 the silk pictures and portraits were made available in postcard form to counteract the decline in popularity of the larger Stevengraphs. These cards included a very collectable series of ships and flags, of which there are about 50 subjects.

Stevengraph bookmarks, despite being quite commonly available and inexpensive (£5-30), have never been widely collected. However, there are many different varieties, and their colourful designs and endearing verses make for an interesting collection.

WOVEN IN PURE SILK.

Above: One of the many historical scenes popular in Victorian Britain. *£50.*

WOVEN IN PURE SILK BY THOMAS STEVENS, STEVENGRAPH WORKS, COVENTRY.

God Speed the Plough.

Right: Idealised country scenes particularly appealed to an increasingly urban Britain. *£100.*

WOVEN IN SILK BY THOMAS STEVENS, INVENTOR AND MANUFACTURER, COVENTRY AND LONDON, (REGISTERED.)

Full Cry.

Above: Hunting scenes were among the most popular of Stevens' output. £50.

THE CRYSTAL PALACE.

Left: Great exhibitions were a favourite Stevengraph subject. £60.

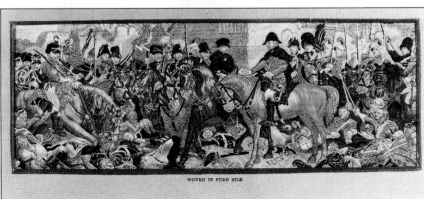

WOVEN IN PURE SILK.

Wellington and Blucher.

MEETING AFTER THE BATTLE OF WATERLOO.

Left: A rousing historical moment. £50.

TABLEWARE

It was not until the mid-17th century that diners used much by way of implements. Before that, food was generally eaten with the fingers off wooden or pewter platters, or even stale-bread 'plates'. During the early 18th century the French and Italian system of laying out a formal table became fashionable in Britain. Large displays of silver and porcelain, and canteens of cutlery (usually sold in sets of 12 seven-place settings), became fashionable.

By the mid-18th century the dining-room table became the stage for elaborate decoration. In France, for example, the centrepiece contained casters and cruets, while in England the epergne had little baskets which could be filled with sweetmeats, pickles or flowers. Cruets contained glass bottles for oil and vinegar, as well as sugar, pepper and mustard-powder casters. Salts were made separately, as historically salt was precious and thought worthy of its own container.

In the early 19th century the emphasis shifted toward self-service at table, and thus entrée dishes, wine coasters, fish slices, pudding trowels and grape scissors became common.

Above: A George III silver sugar basket, the wirework sides with applied husk and floral swags, medallions and a monogram, engraved oval cartouche with ropetwist border, swing handle and detachable clear-glass liner, London, 1774, by William Pinder or William Peavey, 4¼in (10.8cm) high. *£600.*

Above: A pair of silver novelty pepperettes, the hinged visor opening to reveal hollow interior, the centres engraved 'Comrades 1907', Birmingham, 1906, by George Unite. *£320.*

Left: A Dutch silver preserve jar and spoon, pierced interwoven sides revealing a clear-glass liner, beaded scroll handles, floral and leaf border, leaf-chased feet, the domed hinged cover with applied floral finial and engraved crest, the cast leaf spoon with pierced bowl, Rotterdam, *c.* 1810, 4½in (11.5cm) high. *£620.*

Above: A Victorian silver seven-bottle cruet set, oval, floral and leaf-chased sides with central leaf-chased handle, on four pierced scrolling supports, four detachable bottles with silver mounts, Sheffield, 1854, by Martin Hall and Company, 12in (30cm) high. *£420.*

Left: An Estonian silver confiture with matching spoons, vase-form on domed circular foot, the pull-off cover with eagle finial, the everted rim holding eight suspended spoons with prick-engraved borders, *c.* 1780, 9in (22.5cm) high. £650.

Below: A Continental silver biscuit barrel in figure-of-eight shape, the glass body etched with boats, houses, churches, windmills, scrolls and ribbons, with applied pierced base chased with figures in a rural setting, the hinged cover chased with a tavern scene, *c.* 1890, 5¼in (13cm) high. £1,300.

Left: A George III silver-gilt epergne, circular base on three ball feet with waved border and domed centre surmounted by a cast putto with four scrolling reeded arms supporting openwork reeded baskets, with detachable cut-glass bowls, London, 1798, 15½in (39cm) high. £4,000.

Above: A Victorian silver revolving dinner set, gadrooned borders and two scrolling side handles, domed circular base, containing a central circular soup tureen with domed pull-off cover, three rectangular entrée dishes with bayonet handles and gadrooned borders and three pepper pots with pierced covers, 24in (61cm) diam. £850.

TILES

During the 17th and 18th centuries, Delftware tiles were extremely popular in Europe. Delftware is an earthenware pottery which has been coated with a white tin glaze which is then decorated in colours. Although, as its name suggests, it originated in Holland, it was also produced in London, Bristol and Liverpool. Seventeenth-century Dutch Delftware tiles tended to employ fairly simple designs surrounded by scalloped borders, while English designs tended to be more complex and also favoured oriental motifs.

By 1800 the development by the Staffordshire potteries of blue-and-white transfer printing spelled the end for English Delftware, although in Holland it is still produced. Identifying Delftware is difficult, the collector having to research the design, colour scheme and thickness of the tile.

In the 1840s tiles were being mass-produced in Britain, the boom occurring between 1870 and 1910. Minton was the most prolific and produced inlaid, transfer printed, and moulded examples. Other notable manufacturers included H. & R. Johnson, Maw and Company, and Wedgwood. Nineteenth-century tiles are usually marked and dated on the back.

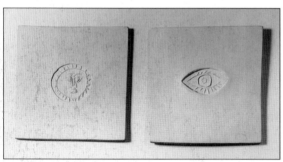

Above: Two tiles from original designs by Picasso, *c.* 1971. *£200-300 each.*

Above: An embossed wall tile by Ruabon Glazed Brick and Fire Clay Ltd, *c.* 1890. *£8-12.*

Left: An English Delftware tile enamelled in manganese, *c.* 1740. *£20-30.*

TINS

Although tinplate was invented in the 17th century, it was not until the 19th century that successful methods of printing on tinplate were developed. First came transfer printing, followed by offset lithography. The result was a vast array of multishaped and multicoloured containers. It was with the advent of the tinplate toy in the latter part of the last century that food manufacturers realised that tinplate toys could serve as an advertising medium as well as a container (the Crawford's biscuit tin omnibus illustrated here is a good example.)

The main focus as far as old and collectable tins is concerned is the biscuit tin (probably the first company to sell biscuits in airtight tins was Huntley and Palmer of Reading in 1846, an innovation partly explained by the fact that the original Mr Huntley's brother, Joseph, owned a metal works next to the biscuit factory). Good 19th-century examples can go for £250 (the Crawford's tin was an exceptional boxed item), but at the other end of the scale it is still possible to pick up pre-World War II cigarette tins for only a pound or so.

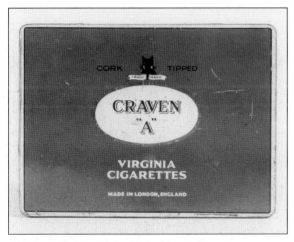

A Craven 'A' cigarette tin. *Under £1.*

Commemorative biscuit tin for the Silver Jubilee of George V. *£15.*

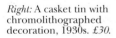

Right: A casket tin with chromolithographed decoration, 1930s. *£30.*

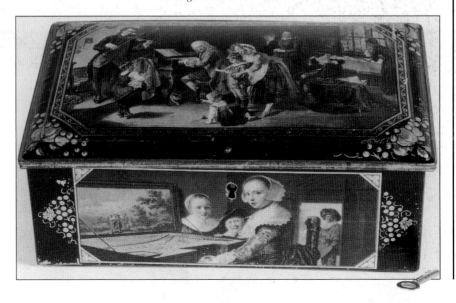

Above: A 1920s tinplate Crawford's biscuit tin, the upper deck hinged to reveal the container, 10¾in (27cm) long. *£1,750.*

Left: A modern American 'Poppy' talcum powder tin. *£2.*

Above: A Classic Curly Cut tobacco tin. *Under £1.*

TOOLS

Hand tools made between *c.* 1750 and the early 20th century are those most sought-after by collectors (all of the items illustrated here fall in that period). It was during this 150 years or so that cabinet-makers and other craftsmen in wood needed fine planes, drills, saws and chisels, and indeed many modern craftsmen like to use 18th- and 19th-century tools for their own work. Apart from their usefulness, tools from this period are also beautiful objects. Made from fine woods such as ebony and walnut, and often bound with brass, they have acquired the lustrous patina of age and use.

The price of tools at auction is still relatively low. For example, a recent sale advertised a 19th-century deal chest containing 31 moulding planes, four chisels and other tools for £100-150 — a small price to pay for such a collection. However, the market for old tools is growing, and prices are set to rise steadily.

Left: A brass-bound saw by Spear & Jackson, Sheffield, England. *£40.*

Right: A moulding plane made by H. Andrews, England. *£65.*

Below: A wood and brass spirit-level by Stratton Bros, Greenfield, Massachusetts, USA. *£100.*

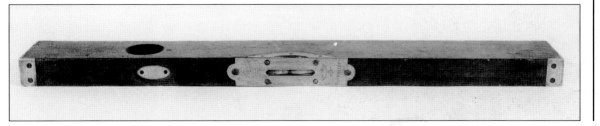

Left: Shoe plane, probably English. £25.

Right: An ebony, walnut and brass brace, probably English. £85.

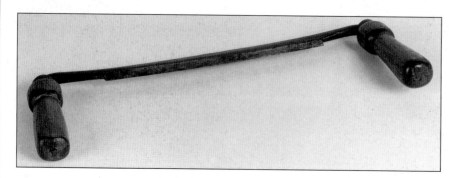

Above: A cooper's plane made by A. Scorby, England. £35.

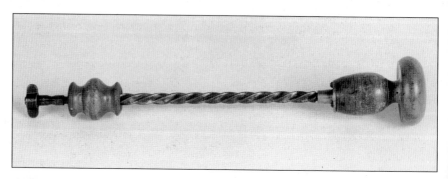

Right: Mechanical screwdriver, English. £15.

TOYS

The fascination with old toys is a relatively recent phenomenon in the antiques world. Perhaps it reflects a growing nostalgia for a time when we, and the world, seemed more innocent and less complicated.

Dolls, teddy bears, trainsets, lead soldiers, die-cast vehicles and tinplate toys form the core of the market, although as each generation of children grows up the range of collectable toys expands to embrace Barbie dolls, plastic soldiers, transformers and the like. This diversity ensures there is something to suit every pocket.

Among dolls it is the wooden, wax and bisque types that are most sought-after. German bisque dolls are the most common, with prices usually ranging between £50 and £1,000.

Teddy bears became popular early in the 20th century. The distinctive German Steiff teddy bears command the most interest and highest prices, while amongst the more affordable are the British Chad Valley and Merrythought products.

Tinplate toys and toy trainsets have been the most popular boy's toys for nearly 100 years. Makers such as Meccano, Bassett-Lowke, Bing, Marklin, Schuco and Marx, and more recently a host of Japanese producers, have supplied many types of brightly coloured toys, often powered by clockwork or battery. These are very collectable, and still represent one of the most imaginative products available to the collector.

Die-cast toys, and in particular Dinky, Corgi, Matchbox and Spot-On products, have attracted tremendous attention since Meccano ceased production in 1979. The condition of these toys is very important, and examples complete with original sale boxes command top prices.

Above: A painted wood doll's house on two floors with a central front door flanked by windows and three windows above, decorated in grey, cream and red, beneath 'tiled' pitched roof with three chimneys, opening to reveal four rooms, upon stand, 24in (60cm) wide x 31in (77cm) high. £300-400.

Above: A German plush-covered teddy bear with cut muzzle, glass eyes, hump and elongated limbs, 28in (71cm) high, probable Steiff c. 1920. £550.

Right: A large clockwork blond plush teddy bear, with long limbs, wide-apart ears, black boot-button eyes, 36in (70cm). £700.

Above, left: A dark gold plush-covered teddy bear, with boot-button eyes, rounded ears and hump, stuffed with straw, 15½in (39cm) high, probably by Steiff. *£700.*

Above, right: Lord Kitchener, a German gold plush-covered teddy bear, with boot-button eyes, stuffed with straw, dressed in khaki felt, 13in (33cm) high, possibly by Steiff. *£400.*

Above: A German blonde plush-covered teddy bear, with pale amber glass eyes, narrow muzzle, hump and felt pads, stuffed with straw, dressed in black and white knitted football jersey and shorts, 14in (35.5cm) high, probably by Steiff. *£150.*

Left: A blond plush German teddy bear with boot-button eyes, black stitched snout and felt pads, 18in (45.5cm) high, probably by Steiff. *£1,400.*

Above, left: A blonde long curly plush-covered Steiff teddy bear, straw stuffed, with elongated limbs, pronounced snout, hump, two-colour eyes, felt pads and Steiff button in ear, 20in (51cm). *£1,000.*

Above, right: A large German blonde plush Zotty type teddy bear, with large rounded ears, amber celluloid eyes, cut muzzle, hump and elongated limbs, stuffed with straw, replaced pads, 28in (71cm) high. *£800.*

Below, left: A rare Emile Jumeau 'Triste' bisque-headed doll, French, 1878, 26in (65cm) high. £12,000.

Below, right: A French bisque-headed doll, c.1870, 17in (42.5cm) high. £1,000.

Above, left: An S.F.B.J. character baby doll, marked 'S.F.B.J. 236 Paris -4-' with open/closed mouth, blue glass sleeping eyes, painted features and blonde hair wig, the bent limbed composition body dressed in a baby gown and leather shoes, 12in (31cm) high. £5,500.

Above, right: A Kammer & Reinhardt German bisque socket-headed character doll, marked 'R Simon & Halbig 117-34' with closed mouth, blue sleeping eyes, fair hair wig, the painted jointed composition body dressed in linen and lace-trimmed undergarments, 13in (33cm) high. £950.

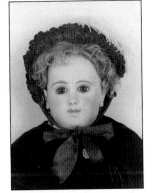

Right: A George II wooden doll, the face with carved nose, lips, ears and small chin, covered in a layer of gesso and painted with rouged cheeks, the inserted black eyes with red dots at the corners and short lashed outline below feather-style eyebrows, the real brown hair wig woven into black cotton cap and secured to head; the body with bust, waist and hips, the arms jointed at shoulder and elbow and ending in elongated fingers, the shaped legs jointed at hip and knee; her original silk gown and skirts with gathered panels, and quilted silk and linen petticoat below, 20in (51cm). £7,500.

Right: Two Kathe Kruse dolls, the painted heads in five sections, each marked in ink on the foot 'Kathe Kruse', *c.* 1925, each 19in (48cm) high. *£2,100 the pair.*

Left: A Simon & Halbig bisque-headed oriental doll with brown eyes and pierced ears, the hair wig arranged in elaborate coiffure with silk flowers and engraved comb, the painted wood and composition body dressed in eau-de-nil and pink silk pantaloon suit with embroidered floral borders edged with gold thread, with gilt buttons, black and red platform slippers embroidered with gold thread, with stand, 20½in (32cm) high, marked '1329 Simon & Halbig'. *£1,300.*

Left: A Simon & Halbig bisque-headed character baby doll with blue sleeping and flirting eyes, quivering tongue and strawberry-blonde wig, the bent limbed composition toddler body with voice box, dressed in cream with quilted silk bonnet 23in (57cm) high, marked 'K * R Simon & Halbig Germany 126 56'. *£400.*

Far left: An Armand Marseille musical marotte, the bisque head with open mouth and upper teeth, fixed blue eyes and blond curls, the body containing the musical movement playing a tune as the wooden stick is twirled, and clothed in a jester's costume, 13in (32.5cm) high. *£250.*

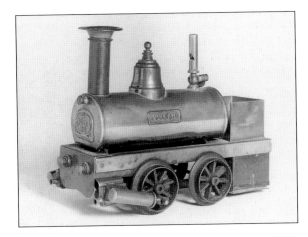

Left: Ernst Plank, a 2½in gauge live-steam, spirit-fired, brass and tinplate 2-2-0 'Vulkan' locomotive, 7¼in (18.5cm) long, some alterations and possibly restored. £200-300.

Below: Bassett-Lowke, an 'O' gauge clockwork Duke of York 4-4-0 locomotive and tender, in maroon livery. £200-300.

Second from bottom, rear group: Part of a Buco trainset, which in total comprises an 'O' gauge No. 304 electric 2-4-2 locomotive, with twin overhead conductors, finished in green livery, boxed; together with a Standard oil tank wagon, red; two Deutsche Reichsbahn lumber wagons; a Bell Kühlwagen, cream, boxed; and SBB CFF passenger coach, and a quantity of track, two Marklin loudspeaker posts, and a signal. £300-500.

Front group: Part of a Bing trainset, comprising an 'O' gauge clockwork G.W.R. passenger set with an 0-4-0 locomotive and tender No. 3410 finished in green livery, two first-class carriages, a goods wagon and tipper wagon, signal sign post, foot-bridge and quantity of track, in original box (lid missing); together with a Chad Valley R.M.S. Queen Mary 'take to pieces' card model, boxed. £200-300.

Right: A Hornby 'O' gauge three-rail electric 4-4-2 Royal Scot locomotive and tender No. 6100, in front of a Hornby No. 4E tinplate station for Ripon. Locomotive: £150. Station: £80.

Above: A Lionel 'O' gauge 3RE double trainset comprising, *top row:* three No. 612 observation carriages with electrically-lit interiors; *middle row:* two 2-4-0 locomotives and tenders; *bottom row:* three Pullman observation carriages with original Ives boxes.
£225 each set.

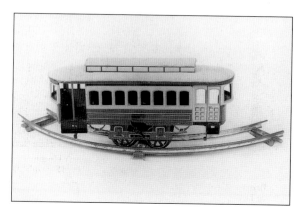

Left: A Bing tinplate clockwork tram No. 10/9221, the vehicle lithographed in yellow and green with orange lining, with a circuit of rails and box, 8½in (21cm) long, one wheel detached. *£300-400.*

Above: Part of a Bing for Bassett-Lowke gauge III trainset, comprising a spirit-fired live steam 4-4-0 'Black-Prince' locomotive and six-wheel tender No. 1902, finished in black with red and white lining, together with a GN open wagon in front of a tinplate Central Station with waiting room and telegraph, and other items, locomotive lacks front bogie and chimney, overall paintwork in need of restoration. *£500-800.*

Below: A Lionel Peter Rabbit Chick-Mobile, the yellow tinplate hand car driven by composition rabbit, composition egg basket to the front, 10in (25cm) long, in original box. *£100-150.*

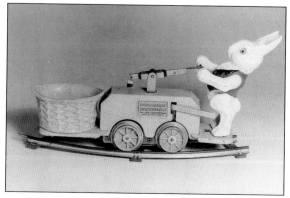

Above: Hausser. A clockwork
four-wheel lorry with
battery-powered mounted
searchlight, with driver and
seven seated artillery men,
together with a flak gun,
with two seated artillery
men, overall length 24½in
(62cm). *£200-300.*

Above: Elastolin. A quantity
of British infantry including
searchlight operator, radio
operator, dispatch riders,
etc., together with German
infantry and band etc.
playworn. *£80-120.*

Left: Britains.The
Village Idiot,
painted with
beige smock and
green breeches.
£75.

Above: Britains. A Home
Farm Series No. 4F, tumbrel
cart and driver. *£50.*

Below: Britains. A 62-piece
Coronation Coach set
including Coldstream
Guards, Household Cavalry,
Royal Fusiliers, Dragoon
Guards, liverymen, mounted
police and eight-horse
Coronation Coach, boxed,
some damage including
coach. *£200-300.*

Above: Britains. Coldstream Guards and bandsmen including three drummers, a bassoonist and three trumpet players. £100.

Below: A collection of German Lineol composition model soldiers including British Army colour guard, British infantry, German Army field dressing station, German Red Cross field ambulance, and French infantry, *c.* 1930. £250.

Left, top: Dinky set No. 2, private automobiles (five in set), *c.* 1960, *£600.* *Middle row, from left to right:* Dinky Connaught racing car, *c.* 1960, *£35.* Dinky Austin Atlantic convertible, *c.* 1960, *£60.* Dinky Mercedes Benz racing car, *c.* 1960. *£35.* Dinky MG Midget, *c.* 1960, *£50.* *Bottom row, left to right:* Dinky Aston Martin DB3, *c.* 1960, *£50.* Dinky Sunbeam Alpine, *c.* 1955, *£50.* Dinky Triumph TR2, *c.* 1960, *£50.*

Left, clockwise from top left: Dinky Foden diesel eight-wheel wagon, *c.* 1955, *£100.* Dinky Foden flat truck with tailboard *c.* 1955, *£80.* Dinky Big Bedford van 'Heinz', *c.* 1955, *£150.* Dinky Foden flat truck with chains, *c.* 1955, *£90.* Dinky A.E.C. Tanker 'Shell Chemicals', *c.* 1955, *£80.* Dinky Leyland octopus wagon, *c.* 1960, *£100.*

Above: A 'Crawford's Biscuits' tinplate omnibus, lithographed in the colours of the London General Omnibus Company, route No. 48, with hinged upper deck revealing biscuit container, 10¾in (27cm) long, with box. *£1,750.*

Left: A Bing tinplate clockwork limousine, with uniformed driver, four opening doors, adjustable windscreen, 14in (35cm) long. *£1,500.*

Clockwise from top far left: Dinky Ford Zephyr, *c.* 1960, £65. Dinky Nash Rambler, *c.* 1960, £50. Dinky Rover 75, *c.* 1955, £65. Dinky Sunbeam Alpine, *c.* 1955, £50. Dinky Leyland octopus tanker 'Esso Petroleum', *c.* 1960, £100. Dinky Foden tanker 'Mobilgas', *c.* 1955, £100. Corgi Standard Vanguard saloon, *c.* 1960, £30. Corgi Jaguar 2.4 litre saloon, *c.* 1960, £35. Corgi Triumph TR2 sports car, *c.* 1955, £35. Corgi Riley police car, *c.* 1960, £30. Dinky A.E.C. tanker 'Shell Chemicals', *c.* 1955, £80. Dinky Leyland octopus wagon, *c.* 1960, £100.

Left top, from left to right: Spot-On ERF 689 flat float, *c.* 1960, £80. Dinky Shell/BP tanker, *c.* 1960, £80. *Second row, left to right:* Corgi Karrier Bantam van, *c.* 1960, £30. Dinky Leyland cement truck, *c.* 1955, £40. Corgi ERF 44G van, *c.* 1960, £60. *Third row, left to right:* Austin-Healey 100-Six, *c.* 1960, £40. Two Corgi Bedford vans, *c.* 1960, £60 the pair. Spot-On Aston Martin DB3, *c.* 1960, £40. *Bottom row, left to right:* Dinky Esso petrol tanker, *c.* 1960, £40. Dinky MG Midget, *c.* 1960, £40. Dinky Castrol tanker, *c.* 1960, £40.

Below: A CIJ clockwork painted tinplate P2 Alfa Romeo, *c.* 1927, finished in red Italian racing colours, with 12-spoke Michelin pneumatic wheels, rear-wheel drive, two leather bonnet straps, operating external hand brake and black steering wheel, 20½in (52cm) long, stamped on base, 'Made in France'. *£1,200.*

Above: Marklin. A Metal Car Construction Set No. 1108G comprising chassis and body work for a Pullman limousine and armoured car. *£1,400.*

Below: clockwise from top:
Straco. A Japanese tinplate battery-operated Bristol Bulldog airplane, 12in (30cm), boxed. *£80-120.*

Tomiyama. A Japanese tinplate battery-operated Astro-Copter, 15½in (39cm), boxed. *£80-120.*

Cragstan. A Japanese tinplate battery-operated United Airways DC7C four-engined mainliner with remote 'U-Control', 17½in (43.5cm) long, boxed. *£150-200.*

Line Mar Co. A Japanese tinplate battery-operated Pan Am Boeing jet airliner, 20in (50cm) long, boxed. *£80-120.*

Above: A pair of Schuco 'studio' Mercedes steerable driving-school racing cars, complete with tools, instructions and sales box. *£90 each.*

Above: An American cast-metal artillery bank, Confederate Army version. If the coin is placed in cannon, when hammer is pushed back and lever pressed it fires coin into rusticated fort, 6in (15cm) high, probably by J. & E. Stevens Co., designed by Peter Adam. *£400-600.*

Right: A Mickey Mouse lithographed and painted tinplate hurdy-gurdy, probably by Distler, winding causes Mickey to turn the organ handle and jointed Minnie Mouse on top of the organ to dance, 8in (20cm) high, some paint rubs. *£720.*

Above: Hess. A printed and painted tinplate two-seater Hessmobil, with clockwork hand-cranked mechanism driving front axle, metal wheels and painted tinplate chauffeur, 9in (23cm) long, marked '3DR PAT 3 DRGM Bᵉ SGDG U.ST PAT' with printed instruction leaflet. *£650.*

TRIBAL ART

Many people are unaware that it is still possible to collect tribal art and ethnographic material. Most of these collectables come from Africa, Indonesia, the Pacific and the Americas. The most sought-after artefacts are those from the 'Pre-Contact' period, i.e. before the arrival of Europeans. Pieces from the last 60-70 years are very much in evidence, but these too can fetch reasonable prices. There is enormous scope in the market for the collector with a small pocket, as well as for those who wish to spend a great deal more in order to expand their collection.

A decorative African mask can be purchased at auction for as little as £30, while several thousand pounds can be spent on a masterpiece of African sculpture. A Mochica stirrup-vessel from South America with colourful painted decoration can fetch around £1,000, while its more decorative counterparts without great age may be around £50. Indonesian and Oceanic material tends to fetch higher prices on the current market, a carved Maori feather box, for example, fetching between £1,000 and £20,000 for a magnificent example. Pieces that were collected around the time of Captain Cook are much sought-after.

So, while many may feel that this is perhaps a rather off-beat area for collecting, the field covers an enormous cross-section of the world's civilisations for which many find a deep empathy.

Above: A Yoruba Gelede mask, the exaggerated ears with interlocking carving in relief, a snail on the right ear, a rabbit on the back, polychrome coloration. £240.

Below: A Cook Island stool, the curved rest supported by four short legs, the feet teardrop-shaped, brown patina, 10½in (42cm). £650.

Left: A Samoan kava bowl, the deep bowl standing on six tapered legs, with lug attachment for sennit hanging, worn patina, 14½in (37cm) diam. £320.

Above: A West African games board, standing on four feet, compartmentalised into 12 sections, with a single large compartment at each end, fine glossy brown patina, 30½in (78cm). £150.

Left: A Cameroonian offering container with diamond-shaped decorative carving, surmounted by a bird, the container supported by a figure standing on a round base, the features highlighted with dark coloration, 20in (51cm). £150.

Above: A Pende stool, the circular rest supported by two figures, the female holding two children, the male with a rounded gourd, worn brown patina, 10½in (26.5cm). £300.

Above: A Senufo rhythm pounder, the male figure standing on the hour-glass shaped pounder, the arms held to the abdomen, scarification incised, elongated facial features, crosshatched coiffure, glossy brown patina, 40⅜in (104cm). £400.

Above, from left to right:
A Thompson River storage basket, the sides and lid decorated with a series of diamond patterns, 18in (45cm). £140.

A Fraser River storage basket of trapezoidal form, the sides with a central geometric pattern, 11in (28cm). £50.

A Fraser River basket of rectangular form, tapering in towards the rim, with bands of contrasting dark brown and sienna fibre, the lid attached with a hide binding, 8in (20cm). £150.

TUNBRIDGEWARE AND TREEN

Tunbridgeware is the generic term given to wooden mementoes made in Tunbridge Wells. The earliest examples date from the 17th century, and they include a variety of items such as tea caddies, needlework boxes, rulers, pen boxes, candlesticks and pin-cushion holders. Such souvenirs often bore the label, 'A Present from Tunbridge Wells'.

Treen is the collective name for small wooden artefacts (such as spoons, boxes, egg-shaped and painted needle cases and painted wildfowl decoys) made originally from native British timber but, from the 18th century, increasingly from imported exotic hardwoods such as ebony and mahogany.

Both Tunbridgeware and treen form a specialist collector's area, and rare or fine examples will command high prices.

Below: A Tunbridgeware jewellery box with a cover of cube parquetry inlay, 7in (18cm) wide. *£110.*

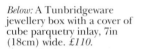

A treen mixing bowl, 14½in (37cm) diam. *£65.*

A Tunbridgeware box banded with yew wood and outlined with barber's-pole stringing, 10½in (26.5cm) wide. *£150.*

WATCHES

The interest in collecting wristwatches is a relatively recent one, and it is an expanding area. The design and appearance of a wristwatch generally has a greater influence on its desirability than its technical qualities. There is a market for examples of all ages provided they have the correct collectable qualities. The main aspects affecting the value of a wristwatch are its case, dial design, technical complication and the maker's name.

Sought-after cases are those that are unusual in shape — not just a standard circle, but square or rectangular. The type of metal used is also important — pink or yellow gold, platinum, or a mixture. Water-resistant cases are especially collectable and command a premium.

The design and quality of the dial is also an influential factor, for example the type of numerals used. Painted dials are more valuable than printed, and restored examples are certainly less desirable. It is worth emphasising that the overall appearance of the watch tends to be more important than technical matters; however the two need to be viewed together in determining value.

Also of importance is the maker's name. Among makers sought-after by collectors are Patek Philippe, Cartier and Rolex — all relatively prolific manufacturers. Smaller makers include Audemars Pignet, Omega, and Vacheron and Constantin.

Above from left to right:
Longines. A 14ct. gold rectangular wristwatch, signed silvered dial with diamond set stud numerals, in a domed case, 39mm x 24mm. *£300.*

Tissot. An 18ct. gold chronograph wristwatch with registers and tachometer, the nickel movement signed Chs. Tissot & Fils, No. 1749582, jewelled to the centre, signed gilt dial with three subsidiaries for 12-hour recording, in a circular case, the buttons in the band, 36mm, import marks for London 1955. *£1,000.*

International Watch Co. An 18ct. gold wristwatch, signed silvered dial with baton numerals and centre seconds, damascened nickel movement jewelled to the centre, in a circular stepped case, 37mm, *c.* 1945. *£280.*

Rolex. An 18ct. gold octagonal lady's wristwatch, silvered dial signed 'Rolex', the Prima movement timed six positions for all climates, in a Rolex case with wheatear engraved band, 22mm, Glasgow 1928. *£400.*

Above top: Ingersoll. A Mickey Mouse wristwatch, the nickel movement with lever escapement, the rotating seconds formed as three running mice, the hands formed as Mickey's hands, in a plain circular case, 32mm, *c.* 1940. *£180.*
Above, bottom: Ingersoll. A nickel-cased Mickey Mouse watch, the machined three-quarter plate movement with keyless lever escapement, the revolving subsidiary seconds with pictures of three mice, 49mm. *£320.*

Right: International Watch Co., Schaffhausen. A matching pair of gentleman's and lady's 18ct. gold wristwatches in presentation box, the gilt serpentine dials signed 'I.W.C. International Watch Co., Schaffhausen', baton numerals, the integral flexible linked bracelets with concealed clasps, in white leather presentation box. *£2,700.*

Above, top left: Rolex. A 9ct. gold rectangular wristwatch, silvered dial signed Rolex, subsidiary seconds, raised gold numerals, the Ultra Prima movement timed six positions, in a case with stepped sides and lug insets, 37 x 25mm, Glasgow 1937. *£550.*

Above, top right: Rolex. A 9ct. gold Oyster wristwatch, the Extra Prima movement timed six positions, signed champagne dial with subsidiary seconds, the case with screw-back and screw-down crown, 32mm, Glasgow 1935. *£720.*

Above, lower left: Rolex. A 9ct. gold octagonal wristwatch, the silvered dial signed 'Rolex Oyster', subsidiary seconds, the Extra Prima movement timed six positions for all climates, the Rolex case with screw-back and screw-down winding crown, 35mm, Glasgow 1927. *£1,450.*

Above, lower right: Rolex. A steel Oyster wristwatch, the silvered dial signed 'Rolex Oyster', subsidiary seconds, the Extra Prima movement timed six positions, in a Rolex case with screw-back and screw-down crown, 33mm, the back dated 1934. *£380.*

Above, centre: Rolex. A steel dress watch, silvered dial signed 'Rolex Prince Imperial', concentric chapter ring at 12 o'clock and subsidiary seconds below, the damascened nickel movement signed

'Rolex Observatory Quality', timed six positions, No. 1000369, in a plain case with semi-circular bow, 42mm; with a steel chain. *£360.*

Right, clockwise from top left: Movado. An 18ct. gold dress watch, signed black dial with subsidiary seconds and raised gold numerals, damascened nickel movement signed 'Movado Factories, Adjust. Temp.' 16 jewels, 43mm. *£320.*

Patek Philippe No. 881744. An 18ct. gold presentation dress watch, the damascened nickel movement signed and numbered, adjusted five positions, jewelled to the centre, signed silvered dial with raised Arabic numerals and signed 'Tiffany & Co.', 45mm. *£750.*

International Watch Co., Schaffhausen. A 14ct. gold hunting cased dress watch, signed silvered dial with raised Arabic numerals, subsidiary seconds, gilded movement jewelled to the centre, 51mm, 1920. *£550.*

Longines. A 14ct. gold bag watch, the signed movement numbered 3737626, three adjustments, the pop-up silvered dial with black-enamel bezel, 42 x 30mm. *£340.*

Above, left to right: Patek Philippe. An 18ct. gold and diamond-set lady's wristwatch, No. 1407442, case no. 2803228, model No. 4498/1, the blue dial signed 'Patek Philippe, Genève', diamond stud numerals, the 18 jewel movement adjusted five positions, in a rounded oblong case, the bezel set with single-cut diamonds, integral flexible bracelet, 21mm. *£2,500.*

Rolex. An 18ct. gold Cellini wristwatch, signed nickel 19 jewel movement with gilt dial, signed 'Rolex, Genève, Cellini', in a rounded rectangular case, heavy mesh integral flexible bracelet, 28mm. *£1,000.*

Rolex. An 18ct. gold and diamond-set Cellini wristwatch, the signed nickel 19 jewel movement with silvered dial signed 'Rolex, Genève, Cellini', baton numerals, in a rounded rectangular stepped case, the sides with double rows of brilliant-cut diamonds, integral flexible bracelet, 28mm. *£1,900.*

Patek Philippe. An 18ct. gold quartz wristwatch, No. 1500498, case No. 2775779, model No. 3744/1, the white dial signed 'Patek Philippe, Genève, Gubelin', roman numerals, in a circular case with milled bezel, integral flexible bracelet, 34mm. *£2,800.*

WOODEN BOXES

The term 'box' can encompass large pieces of furniture, such as the heavily carved oak examples of the 16th century, and the delicate tea caddies of the 18th century. The collector today tends to value the smaller pieces, and it is these that command the higher prices.

In the past, many wooden boxes were made as gifts. They were often intricately decorated with marquetry or silver mounts, and are mainly appreciated for their decorative quality.

Functional boxes, including knife and decanter boxes, and vanity and writing cases, have been produced since the early 17th century and can tell us something about the life of the times: for example, in the 18th century, tea was a very precious commodity and needed to be locked away, so cabinet-makers made special little boxes just for that purpose — tea caddies.

Great 18th-century cabinet-makers such as Chippendale and Sheraton made boxes, and Hepplewhite, for example, made particularly innovatory knife boxes with vase or urn shapes in satinwood, mahogany, chestnut or sycamore, often distinguished by fine marquetry.

Above: A comprehensively fitted coromandel-wood travelling toilet box, the hinged cover opening to reveal an interior fitted with scent bottles and toilet bottles; the top layer on horizontal axis reveals two trays fitted with medicinal and sewing implements; also fitted for writing equipment, the side panels with ivory hand-mirrors, shoe-horn and glove-stretchers, plain silver mounts to toilet bottles etc., monograms to most pieces, London, 1884. *£1,100.*

Left: An Art Deco mahogany and satinwood lady's cabinet, the hinged mirrored top and fall-front revealing a bird's-eye maple fitted interior with drawers and pigeonholes, the fall-front leather-lined for a writing slope, 10⅝in (27cm) high, 15⅜in (39.5cm) wide. *£650.*

Above: A 19th-century boule and rosewood decanter box, serpentine hinged lid and front, with hinged sides and a removable rosewood-veneered tray, holding four cut-glass decanters, decorated with gilt floral sprays, six similar glasses and five others, the case inlaid with foliate-cut brass and tortoiseshell veneer, four waisted feet, with carrying handles, 13in (33cm) wide. *£650.*

Right, clockwise from top left:
A Regency satinwood tea caddy, the hinged rectangular cover inlaid with parquetry, opening to reveal compartments for twin canisters and mixing bowl, 12in (30.5cm) wide. *£110.*

A Regency rosewood tea caddy, opening to reveal a lined interior, the whole inlaid with ebony and ivory stringing, 7¼in (18.5cm) wide. *£140.*

A Regency tortoiseshell tea caddy, opening to reveal twin covers with ivory finials, the whole outlined with ivory stringing, 7¼in (18.5cm) wide. *£600.*

A Regency ivory-veneered tea caddy, opening to reveal a single compartment, the sides veneered with bands of ivory interspaced with ebony stringing, 4¼in (10.5cm) wide. *£340.*

A Regency bronze cassolette inkwell, lifting to reveal a fitted interior with ormolu pounce pot, nib tray and ivory seal, 5⅝in (14.5cm) high. *£190.*

A Regency parquetry tea caddy, opening to reveal twin lined compartments, the whole inlaid with parquetry of various woods, four bun feet, 9in (23cm) wide. *£180.*

Right: A Regency tortoiseshell tea caddy, the hinged cover opening to reveal twin compartments, the covers with turned ivory handles, the whole inlaid with pewter stringing, on four bun feet, 5¼in (13cm) wide. *£500.*

Above, left to right:
A miniature mahogany cabinet, the front with two drawers with swing handles and architrave borders, the whole outlined with barber's-pole stringing, 10in (25cm) wide. *£70.*

A Chinese export lacquered tea caddy, the hinged cover opening to reveal twin pewter canisters with covers, the whole decorated in gilt, with twin carrying handles, 10¼in (26cm) wide. *£130.*

A George III yew-wood work box, the hinged corner opening to reveal the interior, with twin shell-cast handles, on eight ball feet. *£100.*

Right: A Victorian toilet box, comprising: coromandel case, hobnail cut-glass bottles with silver covers with leaves and strapwork, monograms and cartouches, the concealed drawers revealing a mother-of-pearl manicure set, pencil, thimble and sewing set, retailed by Aspreys, in outer leather case. *£2,300.*

Left: A French jewel casket, rectangular silver-plated frame on four ball feet, polychromatic enamelled panels to sides and hinged cover, c. 1880, 6½ x 4¾ x 4¾ in (16.5 x 12.1 x 12.1 cm). £1,200.

Above: An Anglo-Indian carved sandalwood work box and writing slope combined, intricately carved with foliage and exotic birds, opening to reveal a mirror and fitted interior, similarly decorated with ivory fittings, the whole lifting to reveal a hinged slope with pen trays and inkwell, 15in (38cm) wide. £240.

Above: A pair of George III cutlery cases, opening to reveal fitted interiors, the whole outlined with barber's-pole stringing and brass ring handles, 14½in (37cm) high. £950.

Above: A Regency mahogany wine cooler, surmounted by a beaded tablet, the lid with a gadrooned rim above panelled front and sides, 29½in (75cm) wide. £750.

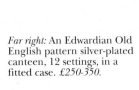

Far right: An Edwardian Old English pattern silver-plated canteen, 12 settings, in a fitted case. £250-350.

FURTHER READING & PLACES TO VISIT

This list covers many of the subjects in this guide but is, of necessity, very selective. There is a vast literature on the different aspects of collecting, and the general titles here have been chosen in the hope that they will lead the reader on to deeper research. Shire Publications Ltd (Cromwell House, Church Street, Princes Risborough, Bucks HP17 9AJ) publish a very extensive list of books covering many of the areas discussed in this guide, and it is well worth getting their catalogue.

Advertising Bygones:
Keith & Penny Gretton, *Advertising Collectables*, B.B.R. Publishing, 1989.

Antiquities:
Charles Ede, *Collecting Antiquities: An Introductory Guide*, Hollington Books, 1984.

Art Deco Figurines:
Bryan Catley, *Art Deco and Other Figures*, Antique Collectors' Club, 1978.

Automobilia:
D. B. Tubbs, *Art and the Automobile*, Arlington Press, 1979.

Buttons:
Primrose Peacock, *Discovering Old Buttons*, Shire Publications Ltd, 1978.

Card Cases and Snuff Boxes:
Eric Delieb, *Silver Boxes*, Exeter Books, 1980.

Ceramics:
Kevin Pearson, *The Doulton Figurine Collector's Guide*, Kevin Francis Publishing, 1988.
Nicholas Pine, *The Concise Encyclopaedia and Price Guide to Goss*, Milestone, 1988.
P. D. Gordon Pugh, *Staffordshire Portrait Figures*, Praeger, 1971.

Costume:
Naomi Tarrant, *Collecting Costume*, Schiffer Publications, 1991.

Fans:
Nancy Armstrong, *Fans*, Souvenir Press, 1990.

Glass:
Ruth Hurst Vose, *Glass*, Ebury Press, 1989.

Gramophones:
Christopher Proudfoot, *Collecting Phonographs and Gramophones*, Studio Vista, 1989.

Inkwells:
Betty & Ted Rivera, *Inkstands and Inkwells*, Crown Inc, 1980.

Jewellery:
Michael Poynder, *The Price Guide to Jewellery, 3,000 BC-AD1950*, Antique Collectors' Club, 1976.

Jukeboxes:
Nick Costa, *Automatic Pleasures*, Kevin Francis Publishing, 1988.

Kitchenalia:
Geoffrey Warren, *Kitchen Bygones: A Collector's Guide*, Souvenir Press, 1984.

Lighting:
Josie A. Marsden, *Lamps and Lighting*, Guinness Books, 1990.

Medical Collectables:
Keith Wilbur, MD, *Antique Medical instruments*, Millbank Books, 1979.

Militaria:
Lawrence Gordon, *British Battles and Medals*, Spink & Son, 1988.
Martin Miller, *Collector's Illustrated Guide to Firearms*, Barrie & Jenkins, 1978.

Model Ships:
Norman Boyd, *The Discovery of Ship Models*, Napier Editions, 1978.

Modern Furniture:
Miriam Stimpson, *Modern Furniture Classics*, The Architectural Press, 1987.

Pens:
Andreas Lambrou, *Fountain Pens*, Vintage and Modern, Southerby's Publications, 1989.

Perfume Bottles:
Jacquelyne J. Jones North, *Commercial Perfume Bottles*, Schiffer Publications, 1988.

Photography:
Elizabeth Martin, *Collecting and Preserving Old Photographs*, Collins, 1988.
J. McKeown, *Price Guide to Antique and Classic Cameras*, distrib. Hove Photo Books, 1985.

Printed Ephemera:
The Guide to Cigarette Card Collecting (annual), Alberts
B. Bennett, *Collector's Guide to Autographs*, Homestead, 1986.
J. H. D. Smith, I.P.M. *Catalogue of Picture Postcards and Year Book* (annual), I.P.M.

Radios:
Jonathan Hill, *Radio! Radio!*, Sunrise Press, 1986.

Railway Bygones:
John Mander, *Collecting Railwayana*, Moorland Publishing Co., 1989.

Samplers:
Averil Colby, *Samplers, Today and Yesterday*, B. T. Batsford, 1984.

Scientific Instruments:
Harriet Wynter and Anthony Turner, *Scientific Instruments*, 1975.
M. Daumas, *Scientific Instruments of the 17th and 18th Centuries*, B. T. Batsford, 1972.

Sewing Collectables:
Gay Ann Rogers, *An Illustrated History of Needlework Tools*, John Murray, 1980.

Silhouettes:
Peggy Hickman, *Silhouettes: A Guide to British Silhouette Portraits,* National Portrait Gallery, 1987.

Smoking Collectables:
Richard Carlton Hacker, *The Ultimate Pipe Book*, Souvenir Press, 1988.

Sporting Bygones:
Louis Stanley, *The Sporting Collector*, Pelham Books, 1985.
John Taylor, *Golf Collector's Price Guide*, St Giles, 1988.

Stevengraphs:
Austin Sprake, *Price Guide to Stevengraphs*, Antique Collectors' Club, 1989.

Tableware:
Harold Newman, *An Illustrated Dictionary of Silverware*, Thames & Hudson, 1987.

Tiles:
Hans van Lemmen, *Tiles: A Collector's Guide*, Souvenir Press, 1990.

Tins:
M. J. Franklin, *British Biscuit Tins, 1868-1939*, New Cavendish Books, 1979.

Tools:
Christopher Proudfoot & Philip Walker, *Woodworking Tools*, Phaidon, 1984.

Toys:
Gwen White, *Antique Toys*, Chancellor Press, 1971.
Opie, Chilcott & Harris, *20th Century Toys*, Letts, 1991.

Tribal Art:
Werner Gillon, *A Short History of African Art*, Penguin, 1991.

Watches:
T. P. C. Cuss, *Antique Watches*, Antique Collectors' Club, 1976.

PLACES TO VISIT

In this highly selective list, those areas of the museums' collections that are of particular interest to readers of this guide have been indicated.

Victoria & Albert Museum
Cromwell Road
London SW7 2RL
(071) 938 8500
Perhaps the world's finest and most comprehensive collection of antiques and collectables, it has examples from almost every section of this book, particularly costume, ceramics, glass, tiles and antiquities.

The Geffreye Museum
Kingsland Road
London E2 8AE
(081) 739 8368
Kitchenalia and old tools.

Science Museum
Exhibition Road
London SW7 2DD
(071) 938 8000
Scientific and medical instruments, tools and radios.

The Museum of London
150 London Wall
London EC2Y 5HN
(071) 600 3699
Tiles and costume.

The National Maritime Museum
Park Row
Greenwich
London SE10 9NF
(081) 858 4422
Model ships, scrimshaw, navigational instruments, nauticalia.

National Motor Museum
Beaulieu
Brockenhurst
Hants SO42 72F
(0590) 612345
Automobilia.

The Mechanical Music and Doll Collection
Church Road
Portfield
Chichester
West Sussex PO19 4HN
(0243) 236 1022
Gramophones, dolls.

Birmingham Museum of Science and Industry
Newall Street
Birmingham B3 1RZ
(021) 236 1022
Pens and writing equipment.

National Army Museum
Royal Hospital Road
London SW3 4HT
(071) 730 0717
Militaria.

Pollock's Toy Museum
1 Scala Street
London W1P 1LT
(071) 636 3452
Toys.

Principal auction houses specialising in collectables:

Bonhams Chelsea
65-69 Lots Road
London SW10 0RN
(071) 351 7111

Sotheby's
34 New Bond Street
London W1A 2AA
(071) 409 2686

Christie's South
Kensington
85 Old Brompton Road
London SW7 3LD
(071) 581 7611

Phillips West 2
10 Salem Road
London W2 4LD
(071) 228 9090

Index

ACKNOWLEDGMENTS

The author wishes to thank Elizabeth Hand and
Alexander Crum Ewing for their hard work and
invaluable help with this book.

In addition, thanks to the following staff at Bonhams
for their assistance and technical advice:

Joanna Black

Juliette Bogaers

Kevin Conru

Joanna Gardner

Matthew Girling

James Hammond

Peter Horner

Charles Langlands Pearse

Graham Lay

Joanna Van Der Lander

Photographers:

Thomas Ward

Roger Dixon

Thanks are also due to Keith Gretton of Keith Old
Advertising who supplied the objects and
photographs for pages 12-15 and 17, Peter Warner of
Holywell Graphics, and Peter Johnson.